BOTTOM LINE/Personal
CONFIDENTIAL REPORTS

Confidential Report #1:

Money Secrets of the Rich
& Well-Connected

Confidential Report #2:

The Doctor's Handbook of
Healing Remedies and
Medical Breakthroughs

Confidential Report #3:

The Bottom Line Guide
to Practically Everything

D1511594

www.BottomLineSecrets.com

Contents

CONFIDENTIAL REPORT #3

THE BOTTOM LINE GUIDE TO PRACTICALLY EVERYTHING

CONFIDENTIAL REPORT #1:

Money Secrets
of the
Rich and Well-Connected

Money Secrets of the Rich and Well-Connected

The Automatic Millionaire's Very Simple Get-Rich Secret

Sticking to a budget means depriving yourself today for the sake of your future well-being. Few of us have the discipline that this requires—we dine at expensive restaurants…buy new cars every few years…and spend $3.50 for a cup of coffee. Result? Even people with decent incomes live from paycheck to paycheck.

To save steadily, most people need to put savings on autopilot. Arrange for a certain percentage of each paycheck to be tucked away. This takes little discipline or effort. You can arrange for your bank or mutual fund firm to automatically take money out of your bank account every month.

HOW MUCH TO SET ASIDE

Start out small. Save 1% of your salary. Soon, you can bump that up to 3%. Your goal should be to save at least 10%. Those with grander objectives should save 15% to 20%. You will be amazed by how little sacrifice is involved.

Say you now buy lunch at the office every day. By brown-bagging it (at a cost of $1 per day instead of $8), you can save $35 a week, or about $150 a month. If you earn a 7% annual return, that savings would grow to $73,791 in 20 years.

The best way to save is with a 401(k) or other tax-advantaged plan. If you save after-tax dollars, the federal government alone takes about $3 of every $10 you earn. When you put $10 into a retirement plan, the entire sum goes to work and won't be taxed until withdrawal.

PAY DOWN YOUR MORTGAGE

Making regular mortgage payments is a form of forced savings.

To accelerate the process, see if your bank will allow you to pay off your mortgage early,

David Bach, founder and CEO of FinishRich, Inc., financial advisers and educators, New York City. *www.finishrich.com.* He is author of *Smart Couples Finish Rich, Smart Women Finish Rich* and *The Automatic Millionaire.* Broadway.

perhaps by making one payment every two weeks instead of one a month. By following this system, you will make 26 half payments, or the equivalent of 13 monthly payments each year. You could pay off a 30-year mortgage in about 23 years.

Consider that a $250,000 30-year mortgage with an interest rate of 6% will cost you $289,595 in interest. By paying biweekly, you will pay $60,972 less.

Are You a Savvy Consumer?

Elisabeth Leamy, an Emmy Award–winning television investigative reporter, Washington, DC. She is author of *The Savvy Consumer: How to Avoid Scams and Rip-Offs That Cost You Time and Money.* Capital. For more quizzes, visit *www.thesavvyconsumer.com.*

As a TV investigative reporter, I see even smart people getting ripped off for thousands of dollars every day.

To avoid being a target, be the hunter, *not* the hunted. Ignore any company that pursues you too aggressively—the contractor who knocks on your door claiming to be working on other houses in the neighborhood...the broker who cold-calls you with must-own stocks...the carpet cleaner who sends you a coupon offering steep discounts. Always conduct your own research first, then hire someone that you have sought out.

To test just how knowledgeable you are as a consumer, take my quiz. *Answer true or false...*

●**When you buy a new car, federal law allows you three days to change your mind and return it.**

False. All car sales are final. Consumers frequently make this mistake because they believe automobiles fall under the Federal Trade Commission's "cooling-off rule." This regulation allows you 72 hours to cancel the purchase of a product—but only if it was sold to you at your home or away from the seller's normal place of business, such as at a hotel or convention center.

The only way you can return a new car is if it qualifies as a lemon under state law. Lemon laws apply only to new cars and vary by state. Typically, you have to prove that the car has had the same problem repeatedly and can't be fixed, or that it has been in a repair shop for a total of more than 30 days within the first 12 months or 12,000 miles. For help in getting the manufacturer to comply with lemon laws, contact your state consumer protection office or use the Better Business Bureau's Auto Line, a free program that helps car owners resolve disputes about defects (800-955-5100, *www.dr.bbb.org/autoline/index.asp*).

●**If your home-improvement contractor rips you off or does shoddy work, some states will pay you back.**

True. Many states have "construction recovery" or "contractor's guaranty" funds that reimburse consumers for as much as $50,000 or more. The fund covers general contractors, plumbers, electricians, etc. Check with the state board of contractors or department of licensing to see if such a fund is available.

Important: To be eligible for reimbursement, you must have hired a contractor who is licensed in your state. (Thirty-six states require contractors to be licensed, and nearly all states license plumbers and electricians.)

You can present your case yourself at a formal hearing and be reimbursed by your state in as little as 60 days.

Helpful evidence: Photos of shoddy work and an inspector's report.

To avoid unlicensed contractors, know the warning signs...

●An unmarked vehicle. Most states require license numbers to appear on vehicles, estimates and advertising.

●The only contact information for him/her is through a post office box, a pager or an answering service, instead of a permanent street address.

●He has a "business" or "occupancy" license, not a contractor's license. A business license is not proof of competency and requires no testing or apprenticeships. An occupancy license is for zoning—it simply grants permission to conduct a certain type of business at a particular address.

•**If you receive unsolicited merchandise in the mail, you are legally obligated to send back the product or pay for it.**

False. Federal law makes it illegal for companies to send you something that you didn't order and then bill you for it. You're allowed to keep the item as a gift, give it away or throw it out. *Other steps to take...*

•Send a certified letter to the company notifying it that you have received unwanted merchandise and will not be burdened with the time and expense of returning it. While you are not required by law to send such a letter, by doing so, you establish a paper trail in case the company ever tries to come after you with collection notices.

•If it appears that you received an item through an honest error—such as a customer mix-up at a legitimate merchant—you can write or E-mail the seller saying that you're giving it a reasonable amount of time (15 to 30 days) to send a courier to pick up the product or else you reserve the right to keep the item. If you receive a bill, contact your local US Postal Inspector's office to report the company.

•**A coupon to clean four rooms of carpeting for $29.95 is a good deal.**

False. Based on my investigations of carpet cleaners, initial low prices with these common come-ons always are followed by hefty "upcharges." Typically, you'll be charged extra for pretreatment solutions, deodorizers and protective spray...moving furniture...and cleaning carpeting in closets.

To avoid rip-offs...

•Use a reputable carpet cleaner. These companies tend to charge by the square foot, not the room. You also may want to hire a cleaning contractor that uses truck-mounted equipment, which is more powerful than the self-contained equipment used by cut-rate carpet cleaners.

•To find a reputable cleaner in your area, contact the Institute of Inspection, Cleaning and Restoration Certification (800-835-4624, *www. iicrc.org*).

•**Your chances of winning a publisher's sweepstakes increase if you buy a magazine.**

False. More than half of American adults entered a sweepstakes in the past year. What many don't realize is that, by law, sweepstakes mail offers must give you an equal chance of winning, regardless of whether you purchased anything.

Know these rules...

•When representatives for legitimate sweepstakes promotions call, they cannot describe the prize before making their sales pitch.

•After the sales pitch, they must reveal the retail value of all prizes and disclose your odds of winning, when the prizes will be awarded and how to get a list of winners.

•They cannot claim that you have won a prize unless you really have. Promoters often get around this rule by claiming that you have won a "free vacation offer," not a free vacation.

Important: Don't make up-front payments. Promoters of legitimate sweepstakes never ask for money to cover taxes and processing, judging or entry fees.

If you suspect fraud, contact your state's attorney general or secretary of state.

•**When you get an unwanted telemarketing pitch, you should say, "Take me off your list."**

False. That request has no legal teeth. *Better...*

•Ask the telemarketer to put you on the company's "do-not-call" list. Laws require telemarketers to maintain and honor such lists.

•Have your home and cell phone numbers put on three do-not-call lists—the Direct Marketing Association list, 212-768-7277, *www.the-dma. org*...your state's "Do-Not-Call" Registry (contact your state consumer protection agency office to find out if your state has one)...FTC's National Registry, 888-382-1222, *www.donotcall.gov.*

•**Parking garage time clocks are accurate.**

False. When I investigated parking garages around Washington, DC, I discovered that 75% of them skewed their clocks in their favor by at least six minutes.

Typical result: A customer checks in, returning just before an hour has elapsed, only to be charged for some or all of the second hour.

To avoid rip-offs...

•Make a note of the time on your own watch as you enter and exit, and show the attendant. It doesn't matter whether the garage clocks match yours. What matters is the time elapsed.

•If there is a discrepancy, complain and threaten to contact the department of consumer affairs in your city or town. Most garages will back down rather than risk having an official complaint lodged against them.

●You can improve or repair your credit score within 24 to 72 hours.

True. While the credit repair industry is riddled with scams, "rapid rescoring" is a legitimate service offered by local credit bureaus when you apply for a home loan.

How it works: Rescorers work directly with the three major credit bureaus. Not only do they correct errors on your credit report, they restructure your debt in ways that boost your credit score.

Cost: About $200. This might seem high, but by raising your credit score, you often can qualify for a lower mortgage rate and save thousands of dollars.

How it might work: A rescorer notices that you have three credit cards. One is near its limit, while you hardly use the other two at all. By transferring some debt to the underused cards, you improve your score by 5%. Why would this be? Scoring models are biased against consumers who are near any of their credit limits.

If you want assistance from a rapid rescorer, ask your mortgage broker or lender to refer you to one—rapid rescoring firms don't work directly with consumers. If you get an unsolicited offer for overnight credit repair, it's a scam.

What to Do with Reward Points

Pay your American Express bill with reward points. American Express will accept its own membership rewards points for bill payment, at the rate of 20,000 points for a $100 credit. Consider the Amex offer if you have more reward points than you can use, can't get a free ticket to a preferred destination or don't plan to travel by plane. (A total of 20,000 to 25,000 points earns an airline ticket worth much more than $100.)

Tim Winship, editor, FrequentFlier.com, Web site that provides frequent-flier program information and advice, Los Angeles.

Painless Ways to Save

Mary Hunt, founder and publisher of the newsletter *Debt-Proof Living*. She is author of *Live Your Life for Half the Price (Without Sacrificing the Life You Love)*. DPL Press.

For those people who are trying to stretch their cash, here are some easy suggestions on how to cut costs…

HOLIDAY TURKEYS

Frozen turkeys are much fresher than fresh turkeys. How is that possible?

Modern equipment flash freezes the turkey within minutes of processing.

Freezing does not change the taste or quality. And buying a frozen bird during "turkey season" saves you 50% to 75% of the cost of a fresh turkey.

Never pay for a "name brand." While there are many major brands of turkey, most are processed at one of the five major turkey processing plants in the United States.

GASOLINE

You can earn free gasoline when you go grocery shopping. Large supermarket chains, such as Kroger, Meijer, Raley's, Randalls and Tom Thumb, now give vouchers for discounts at participating stations.

How it works: Purchase any of several hundred products whose brands participate in the "Fuel Rewards" program. With your receipt, you get a voucher for free gas. It is valid for 30 to 60 days, depending on the grocer.

Recent examples: At Kroger stores, buy two packages of Angel Soft double-roll bath tissues and earn $1.25 in gas. Two Mrs. Paul's Frozen Seafood Entrées (Select Variety) earn you $2.25 in gas.

Note: The actual products will vary. Different stores have different items at different times.

For more information: Dallas-based Centego Marketing, 800-281-7118, *www.fuelrewards.com*.

BOOKS

●Booksfree.com. Instead of paying retail or getting on long waiting lists for books at public libraries, you can choose from this pay library's great selection of books. Includes 69,900 titles (fiction, nonfiction, audio and children's books) for a flat monthly fee ($7.99 for books, $19.99

for audiobooks). Each book can be purchased for up to 30% off list price.

How it works: You receive two books at a time through regular mail. There are no due dates, late fees or shipping costs.

When you finish, return the books in a pre-paid mailer. You can cancel your membership at any time without paying a penalty. *www.books free.com.*

Alternative: Buy new and used titles at Half. com, a division of eBay, for 50% to 70% less than retail stores. *www.half.ebay.com.*

TELEPHONE

•**Cheap overseas calls.** Onesuite.com, *www. onesuite.com* (2.2 cents/minute to the UK, 3 cents/minute to Germany)…Kallcents.com, *www.kall cents.com* (6 cents/minute to Hong Kong). You buy minutes in advance and receive a toll-free access phone number.

ENERGY/UTILITIES

•**Use less hot water.** Set your soap dispenser or soap dish on the left side of the sink in your kitchen and bathroom, as close to the hot-water handle as possible.

You, family members and visitors will reach for the cold faucet handle automatically. Cool water is just as effective for cleaning your hands as hot water.

AUTOMOBILES

•**Rent out your garage.** If parking spaces are at a premium in your neighborhood, you could collect $100 or more per month just for parking your own car on the street or in your driveway.

Specify that the arrangement is "for storage only"—no work can be done on the car there. Post a sign on your lawn or place an ad in your local newspaper.

•**Get the most from insurance claims.** If a driver damages your car, you may be able to file a claim for "diminution of value" against his/her insurance company. You might have to provide photos, *Blue Book* values, appraisals, etc. Check with your insurance agent.

Reason: Even though your car was repaired adequately, it has diminished resale value, for which you may be compensated.

Easy Ways to Cut Your Expenses

Jonathan D. Pond, president, Financial Planning Information Inc., Nine Galen St., Watertown, MA 02472. He is author of *Your Money Matters* (Putnam) and *1,001 Ways to Cut Your Expenses.* Dell.

In virtually every part of our lives, we can find easy ways to reduce the cost of living. Housing, clothes, cars and leisure activities all take a large portion of our paychecks. Even our pets cost money to feed and keep healthy.

A little forethought can help us cut our expenses significantly without depriving us of anything we really need. And don't think cutting out the small things won't help save money. Small savings actually compound over the years to produce big savings.

Proven ways to cut costs and get the most for the money you must spend…

HOUSING EXPENSES

•**Don't buy the most expensive home in the neighborhood if you're relocating.** And—don't improve your home so much that it becomes the fanciest one on the block.

Money-saver: Buy a multifamily dwelling and rent out the other units. That way, other people will be paying part—or all—of your mortgage costs.

Alternative: Take in a boarder.

•**If you purchase a condo, do not choose one in a brand-new condominium community.** The maintenance fee won't be predictable. It could go way up.

•**Obtain several bids on home-repair and improvement projects.** After seeing the best offer, ask the other bidders if they can do better—and even after deciding, try to negotiate a still better price with the chosen contractor.

BREAKDOWNS AND CRISES

•**Learn to make emergency repairs yourself.** That way, if a water pipe suddenly bursts or your power fails, you will be able to take swift action to prevent the problem from becoming worse—and more expensive to fix. Buy the necessary fix-it books, tools and supplies.

•**Make an inventory of all your household possessions.** And—save receipts for all major purchases. Keep copies in your safe-deposit box or office. If disaster strikes, you will be able to show the insurance company what you owned and how much it cost.

•**Never assume that a broken appliance must be replaced by a new model.** If you can't get it repaired under the warranty, spend a little to discover exactly what is wrong and how much it will cost to make it usable. And if it can't be fixed, consider doing without it.

Money- and time-saver: Keep all your warranties and owner's manuals in one file.

CLOTHING EXPENSES

•**Find a good tailor who can alter garments that you can no longer wear** because they are out of style or your size has changed…a good shoe repair person who can extend the life of your shoes…and buy clothes that do not require dry-cleaning.

•**Time purchases.** Before buying any clothes, ask the salesperson if and when they will be going on sale.

SHOPPING EXPENSES

•**Make a shopping list.** Set a spending budget before you go shopping for anything…and stick to it.

•**Check classified ads and thrift stores for used furniture.** The best buys are likely to be found in upper-class neighborhoods.

Other furniture money-savers: Visit several discount furniture showrooms…consider buying brand-name furniture by mail or over the Internet where some great bargains are available.

•**Shop for major appliances near the end of the month, quarter or year.** That is when sellers are most anxious to push merchandise out the door to meet sales quotas or win awards.

•**Don't buy service contracts.** The seller expects to make money on them, so premiums are set higher than the average purchaser is likely to spend on repairs.

CAR EXPENSES

•**Buy a good used car instead of an expensive new car.** Keep the car until it costs more to keep it running than to replace it.

Money-saver: If you want a near-new model, ask the dealer about a demonstrator car with a new-car guarantee…or a low-mileage vehicle from a rental agency.

•**If you must buy a new car, be sure to do your homework.** Research all the incentives available on different models that meet your needs. Shop around among different dealers, and consider using an auto brokerage service to get the very best deal available.

Money-saver: The best time to buy is at the end of the model year…or at the beginning of the next model year, when the dealer is even more desperate to get rid of his/her old stock.

•**Keep your car in good shape so that it lasts longer.** Check the level of oil and other fluids weekly…change oil according to the manufacturer's specifications (or even more often)…and check tire pressure and condition frequently.

•**Choose the highest deductible you can live with on your auto insurance.** Reduce your premium further by buying antitheft devices…inquiring about discounts for low annual mileage or for taking a defensive driving course…or asking about discounts for student drivers with good grades or who are away at college.

Money-saver: If your car is worth less than $2,000, drop the collision and/or comprehensive coverage.

LEISURE AND ENTERTAINMENT

•**Eat at home instead of going out.** If you crave a change in diet, buy inexpensive take-out food. If you must go to a restaurant, choose an inexpensive one. Check the price range before you go.

•**When you eat out, don't order more food than you can eat.** If you do, take it home. Don't order the most expensive dishes on the menu.

Money-saver: Split the dessert.

Better still: Eat dessert at home.

•**Drop memberships in clubs**—social, country or athletic—you don't visit frequently.

•**Watch out for book and music clubs.** Don't join clubs that offer you 10 items for a dollar—or even a penny—if you have to agree to buy more books at the club's regular prices. If you figure out the average price of all the required purchases, including postage and handling, it is likely to be higher than you would pay at a discount store. Instead, borrow books and music from your local public library—for free.

PETS

•**Adopt a companion from an animal shelter** instead of buying one at a pet shop.

•**Choose a smaller animal.** It requires less food than a bigger one. Buy generic pet food rather than expensive brand-name food.

Five Reasons to Splurge On a New Car

Eric Peters, a Washington, DC–based automotive columnist and author of *Automotive Atrocities: The Cars We Love to Hate.* MotorBooks International.

From a strictly financial standpoint, it pays for most people to buy used cars. *But five engineering improvements might make it worthwhile for you to consider a new model...*

•**Safer brakes.** Today, even many economy cars have four-wheel disc brakes, and antilock brake systems are becoming common. *Brake Assist*—a new feature that further reduces stopping distances during emergency braking—also is being featured in family cars from Toyota, Volvo and others. Brake Assist automatically applies full pressure to the system during an emergency stop if the driver fails to depress the brake pedal fully. This slows the car more quickly.

•**Intelligent navigation systems.** The latest in-car satellite navigation systems can direct you around traffic jams and help you find the best route to your destination. Real-time data about traffic conditions is uploaded into the system automatically every few minutes via the car's onboard satellite radio hookup. That data is compared against your planned route in the global positioning satellite (GPS) navigation computer. If there's a bottleneck ahead, an alternate route is displayed. Cadillac CTS and Acura RL offer this technology on some newer models. Intelligent GPS should filter down to less expensive models within a year or two.

•**Bodies that don't rust—and paint jobs that last.** Today's cars are so well-protected against rust by multiple coats of protective undercoating and chip-resistant primers that body rot is becoming as rare a sight as a wood-paneled Pacer.

•**Engines that don't pollute.** At least 95% of the combustion by-products of any newer model-year car is harmless water vapor and carbon dioxide. Several models from Ford, General Motors, Honda, Toyota and Volvo qualify as ultra-low emissions vehicles (ULEVs), with virtually no harmful emissions.

•**Decent gas mileage.** Even the worst offender two-ton V8 sport-utility vehicle can get mileage per gallon (mpg) in the mid-teens on the highway. And American drivers no longer have to cram themselves into microsized subcompacts to get 30 mpg.

Vastly improved fuel economy with little difference in size, power or performance can be credited to electronic fuel injection and the widespread use of overdrive transmissions. Both reduce engine operating speeds (and thus fuel consumption) once a vehicle has reached road speed. Seven-speed automatics (BMW and Mercedes-Benz) and continuously variable transmissions (CVTs) hold the promise of further mileage improvements. CVTs deliver the fuel economy of a manual transmission with the ease of an automatic.

How to Travel Free

Robert William Kirk, author of *You Can Travel Free.* Pelican Publishing Co.

There are hundreds of budget guides that tell you how to cut costs on trips. Many of these books contain low-cost travel tips, but they don't give you the ultimate scoop on *no-cost* travel. Instead of traveling cheap, you could be traveling free—from transportation by air or sea to lodgings, meals and entertainment. Most free travel requires no special skills, credentials or contacts. And it can be just as luxurious—and often more pleasurable—than the most expensive paid vacation.

COMPLIMENTARY CRUISES

Cruise lines generally offer a free passage to anyone who recruits 10 to 15 paying passengers. (Many airlines offer similar deals.) If you can't lure that many customers, you can get a pro-rated reduction on your fare.

You can also cruise free as an expert in a pertinent subject. Historians, anthropologists, naturalists and ornithologists are in especially high demand. Your job on the cruise would be to present a series of lectures and to be available for informal questioning. It helps to have a PhD (or at least a master's degree) and to have published articles on the subject, but an affable personality and a willingness to share your knowledge with others can stretch your credentials. After your first cruise in this capacity, a good reference will ease the way at other lines.

Free cruises are also available to doctors and nurses who are willing to be on 24-hour call (here a salary is an added inducement)…to athletic directors and coaches who can help organize recreational activities…to musicians and entertainers willing to perform…to cosmetologists who can barter their services for a ride.

There is also a strong demand for "hosts"—distinguished single gentlemen who are usually age 55 and older. They serve by dining and dancing with the many unattached older women taking these vacation cruises. Besides free room and board, hosts are encouraged to make use of an unlimited bar tab available for themselves and their new female friends.

FREE FOREIGN TOURS

Enlist enough people and get a whole trip—long or short—free. Some travel agencies recruit teachers, who receive a free trip if they bring six students. With 12 students, the teacher's spouse also travels free.

The same deal is available to anyone willing to organize a special-interest tour. An auto racing fan might lead a group to Le Mans…an opera aficionado might arrange a trip to La Scala in Milan. Similar trips focus on photography, architecture, theater, music, golf or wine tasting. The group leader sets the itinerary, chooses lodgings and arranges for side trips. Travel experience and linguistic skills are usually helpful, but not essential.

Travel Savings

Tom Parsons, editor of *Bestfares.com*, a clearinghouse of hidden travel deals, 1301 S. Bowen Rd., Suite 490, Arlington, TX 76013. 800-880-1234. He travels about 100 days a year and currently has about 600,000 frequent-flier miles.

Traveling can be expensive. *Following are a few suggestions on how to save money when booking a hotel and reserving a rental car…*

HOTELS

•**Book your reservation after joining a discount club.** Many hotels list as many as 10 to 12 different rates *per room*. Calling the hotel directly gives you a better chance to get a lower rate than the one offered through the hotel's 800 number.

And even better than calling the hotel is joining a discount club. These clubs are run by national hotel chains and offer members hotel-room discounts of up to *50% below most other rates*. Call several national hotel chains to determine their club fees, benefits and restrictions.

•**Save up to 50% by going through a hotel broker.** Hotel brokers book rooms in hundreds of hotels around the country. Because of the volume they handle, hotels give them steep discounts on rooms. *Examples…*

•Accommodations Express, 800-444-7666, *www.accommodationsexpress.com*.

•Central Reservations Service, 800-555-7555, *www.crshotels.com*.

•Hotels.com, 800-246-8357, *www.hotels.com*.

•Quickbook, 800-789-9887, *www.quickbook.com*.

RENTAL CARS

•**Check the rates offered by all of your frequent-flier accounts.** Not all airline frequent-flier plans offer the same car discounts at the same time.

Example: One company's daily rate at Washington's National Airport recently was $36/day if you belonged to one airline's frequent-flier plan. The same car was $20/day for another airline's frequent-flier plan members.

Make a list of your frequent-flier programs. Then call the car rental firm's main number, and make a list of the different plans' discounts.

.Use the Internet to reserve rental cars.
Like airlines, rental car companies are eager to
promote their Web sites. Many rental-car sites
offer great discounts or free upgrades if you
book over the Internet.

Example: One aggressive rental-car agency
on the Web recently offered discounts of up to 40%
off list rates.

Secrets to Predicting
The Stock Market

Jeffrey Hirsch, president of The Hirsch Organization, an investment research firm, 184 Central Ave., Old
Tappan, NJ 07675. He and his father, Yale Hirsch, edit
Stock Trader's Almanac. John Wiley & Sons. They also
publish *Almanac Investor Newsletter.* Their Web site is
www.stocktradersalmanac.com.

Stock market gyrations aren't entirely random. For nearly 40 years, *Stock Trader's
Almanac* has offered amazingly reliable
indicators of market performance.

Consult a financial adviser if you have questions or trends seem contradictory. You still need
to analyze individual stocks before you start investing in them.

THE JANUARY BAROMETER

The stock market usually sets its direction for
the whole year in January.

The S&P 500 Index has reflected this tendency
92.3% of the time since 1950. Eleven bear markets out of 17 began with a poor January.

BEST SIX MONTHS FOR INVESTING

Since 1950, the stock market has performed
best from November through April and worst
from May through October.

Only twice since 1950 has the Dow posted a
double-digit loss during the November-through-
April period—in 1970, during the invasion of
Cambodia, and in 1973, during the OPEC oil
embargo.

DECEMBER'S FREE LUNCH AND
THE SANTA CLAUS RALLY

Investors typically dump losing stocks in December in order to realize tax losses. By late
December, many stocks have been hammered
down to bargain levels.

The New York Stock Exchange stocks selling
at their 52-week lows near the end of December usually outperform the market by Febru-
ary. Over 29 years, these stocks have averaged
a 13.9% increase in that short span, compared
with the NYSE Composite, which gained 4.2%
over the same period.

A short but robust rally during the last five
days of December and the first two days of January—the Santa Claus rally—comes to Wall Street
most years.

Since 1969, the gain from this rally has averaged 1.7% over just those few days. There have
been 25 Santa Claus rallies in the last 33 years.

Beware of Santa's claws: When there's no
Santa Claus rally, trouble often is ahead. Hence
the couplet—*If Santa Claus should fail to call,
bears may come to Broad and Wall* (where the
New York Stock Exchange is located).

There was no Santa Claus rally in 1999. The
bear market began on January 14, 2000.

PRE–ST. PATRICK'S DAY
RALLY

Experienced traders know that the market often rallies before major legal holidays. People
are about to get time off, so they feel upbeat.
Most traders don't realize how strong the market
is the day before St. Patrick's Day—which isn't a
legal holiday but is celebrated by many.

Going back to 1953, the S&P 500 has gained
an average of 0.33% on that day—equal to a 30-
point advance for the Dow at today's levels.

I view this indicator just for fun, but some
people do make money by following it.

DOWN FRIDAY
AND MONDAY

Trouble often looms when stock prices are
down sharply on both a Friday and the following Monday—six times out of seven, the market
will go lower within five days.

In 1987, the Dow lost 108 points on Friday, October 16, and 508 points the following Monday.

Insider Trading Alert

Beware of insider trading if you work for—or have access to information on—a public company. To avoid this illegal act, ask anyone who gives you a stock tip where he/she got the information. Make sure the information is either publicly available or is the result of independent research and that there is no agreement to keep the information confidential. Never give inside information to anyone, even your spouse. Don't encourage family members to buy or sell stock in your company—the transactions may look suspicious even if they are innocent. Learn your company's trading policies when you buy or sell stock shares.

Dan Brecher, an attorney specializing in claims against stockbrokers, New York City.

Six Secrets for Winning In Any Market

William J. O'Neil, chairman and founder, Investor's Business Daily, Los Angeles, www.investors.com. He is author of How to Make Money in Stocks and The Successful Investor (both from McGraw-Hill).

Bill O'Neil, founder of *Investor's Business Daily*, has a unique stock-selection system. He chalked up a six-year cumulative gain of 705% during the crazy years from 1998 through December 31, 2003, versus the S&P 500 Index's 14.6% for the same period. O'Neil's approach has been labeled one of the most consistent in both bull and bear markets by the American Association of Individual Investors.

O'Neil's rules for determining what to buy and sell are based on his research into the characteristics of winning stocks before they made their greatest price moves. *Following are a few of his rules...*

•**Look for the leader.** Finding turnaround plays is difficult. You're better off buying stocks that are the leading performers in the market—not necessarily recognized names, but those with phenomenal earnings and price performance.

The great stocks I studied had gains of at least 25% in the latest few quarters and on an annualized basis for the three years before their big price surges. When a company is growing by 25% a year, its profits are actually doubling every three years.

Helpful: Stock tables in *Investor's Business Daily (IBD)* include Smart-Select® Ratings for such factors as earnings per share (EPS). Ratings are on a scale of 1 to 99. Thus, an EPS of 80 shows that a stock's earnings growth is outperforming that of 80% of the market. Choose stocks that have EPS ratings of 80 or more.

•**Forget buy low/sell high.** In my 30 years of managing portfolios, I have never bought a stock unless its price was at or within 15% of its 52-week high. History has shown that the best stocks begin their big runs after trading near or above that level.

Look for stocks that have price gains in the top 20% of the market over the last 12 months. This measure of relative price strength (RS) is listed in *IBD* (and 52-week highs are listed in most major papers and on Web sites such as *www.investors.com*).

It is best to choose stocks that have RS ratings of 80 or more.

•**Make charts your friends.** You wouldn't trust a doctor to diagnose your fractured elbow without an X-ray. Nor should you trust yourself to pick stocks without consulting stock charts.

By studying a chart, you learn the character of a stock. Is it volatile or steady? You also get a sense of where it is relative to its past.

If the price has been moving up for a long time without a break, the stock might be vulnerable to a fall. If it has traded in a steady range, it is more likely to make a brand-new move upward.

•**Follow the smart money.** Institutions (mutual funds, banks, pension funds, etc.) make up the bulk of trading in the market because they control such huge sums. If you zero in on stocks that are getting attention from institutions, you stand to make money.

Look for spikes in trading volume (also listed in financial newspapers and on Web sites such as *www.investors.com*) on days when the stock price increases. This means that institutions are scooping up shares.

•Get to know your stocks. Learn as much as you can about a company—its products, customers and reputation. Read annual reports, or go to archives on company Web sites. This will give you more conviction about your decisions.

Always be wary of any product you are convinced is the "next big thing." Your stock should continue to prove itself with above-average price performance.

•Follow sell rules without fail. You aren't going to be right in all of your selections. Don't become too attached.

•First sell rule. Always sell a stock if it falls by 7% to 8% from your purchase price.

•Second sell rule. Sell a stock when it is up by 20% to 25%.

Following these sell rules means that you can be right two out of three times and still make money. *Here's the math...*

You invest $100 in a stock and sell it after you've earned 25% ($25). You invest $125 in another stock and sell it after you earn 25% ($31.25). You invest $156.25 ($125 + $31.25) in a third stock, which you sell at an 8% loss ($12.50). You end up with $143.75—which still represents a 44% gain on your original $100 investment.

How to Protect Your Stock's Value

You can protect the value of your stock by using options.

Example: If a stock is priced at $100/share, buy *put options* that give you the right to sell the stock at $90/share within 12 or 24 months. Then sell *call options*, which let someone else have the right to buy your stock at $120/share over the same period. This structure is called a *collar*. The cost of the put and the proceeds from the call should be equal to limit your downside and ensure that you get at least $90 a share. If the stock price falls below $90, you still can sell it for $90. If it rises above $120, you can sell it or buy back the call option.

Caution: Options trading is complex—consult a knowledgeable financial adviser.

Christopher Cordaro, CFA, CFP, Regent Atlantic Capital LLC, Chatham, NJ.

How to Protect Yourself from Bad Broker Advice

If you lost money as a direct result of a broker's advice, you may be able to recover some of it through arbitration. But you must be able to prove you bought the stock based directly and solely on the broker's flawed recommendation. Write a letter of complaint to the firm. If the matter is not resolved to your satisfaction within two months, file an arbitration claim quickly. Investors recover about half of their money more than half the time in securities arbitration.

To file a claim: The National Association of Securities Dealers provides rules and filing costs for NASDAQ and AMEX claims. Go to *www.nasd.com* and click on "Arbitration & Mediation." For NYSE filings, call 212-656-2772 or go to *www.nyse.com/regulation.*

David E. Robbins, Esq., Kaufmann, Feiner, Yamin, Gilden & Robbins, LLP, and author of the *Securities Arbitration Procedure Manual.* Lexis Law.

An IRA Loophole that Sounds Almost Too Good to Be Legal

Contributions to an IRA must be in *cash only* (since 1987, gold or silver coins of the US can be used; bullion after 1997), not stocks, bonds or other property. And if you sell anything to raise your contribution, you must pay tax on any capital gain.

Tip: Sell stocks that have *declined* in value. You can fund the IRA and also get a capital loss on the sale. Furthermore, if you desire, your IRA can repurchase the stocks immediately. The wash-sale rules shouldn't apply, as you and your IRA are separate legal entities.

It's Not Too Late! You Can Still Build A Solid Nest Egg

Economist, attorney, actor and comedian Ben Stein, who lives in Beverly Hills, CA, with his wife and teenage son. He was a speechwriter for presidents Richard Nixon and Gerald Ford. He is author of *Yes, You Can Become a Successful Income Investor! Reaching for Yield in Today's Market*. Hay House.

Only 18% of American workers have retirement savings of more than $100,000. Less than half have even calculated how much they will need for retirement.

Rectifying this situation has become a personal mission for economist Ben Stein. The notoriously frugal Stein based his Emmy Award–winning TV game show, *Win Ben Stein's Money*, on his passion for saving. Most recently, he served as spokesman for National Retirement Planning Week, sponsored by a coalition of financial education organizations, and testified before Congress about America's retirement savings problem.

Stein answered some questions about America's growing retirement crisis and how he is investing his money...

●**Can Americans count on the Social Security privatization plan to boost their savings?** No. It's actually a distraction from real retirement planning. Squeezing extra returns from your government benefits—the average payout for retirees currently is just $958 per month—is not going to enable you to retire comfortably. That will happen only if you make saving an everyday priority.

●**How much do you put away?** I have been worrying about my retirement since I was 13. I'm 60 now, and although I expect a modest pension from the Screen Actors Guild, I'm also trying to save very aggressively on my own—about 20% of my annual income.

●**Few people can afford to save that much. How can the average person squirrel away more money?** Look, people in China, which has only 14% the gross domestic product per capita that we have, save 40% of their incomes. Americans save roughly 1%, so we can do a lot better.

A clear-cut goal makes it easier to deprive yourself of indulgences. You can calculate how much you will need in retirement at the AARP Web site, *www.aarp.org/money/financial_plan ning*. Be sure to use 100% of your current living expenses as your goal.

You can live on less—but a man of 65 today is likely to live to 80...a woman of 65 is likely to live to 83½. Prices could increase by 75% or more by then, so you must generate income in excess of what you need today.

●**Where do you invest additional money after you have maxed out retirement plan contributions?** Any additional money goes into variable annuities. That advice came from my father, who served as chairman of the Council of Economic Advisors under presidents Nixon and Ford. He did not earn a lot of money in his lifetime, but he had a comfortable retirement because owning annuities meant that he never had to worry about outliving his money.

●**Haven't a lot of people been burned by variable annuities?** Annuities have taken a lot of heat in recent years because of overaggressive selling by the insurance industry and lots of hidden fees. But if you do your homework, you'll realize that transferring the financial risk of living a long life to the insurance company and away from yourself is worth a look. For a primer on annuities, visit *www.sec.gov/investor/pubs/ varannty.htm*...or research low-cost offerings from TIAA-CREF (800-842-2776, *www.tiaacref. org*) and The Vanguard Group (877-662-7447, *www.vanguard.com*).

●**How do you invest your retirement money?** I have always been very diversified, so I have never suffered a catastrophic loss. I spread my money around the way a large institutional investor does. I use different brokerage firms. I manage some of my accounts myself...I hire money managers for others. I own wide-ranging global asset classes—from emerging-market bonds to real estate investment trusts (REITs).

●**What mistakes have you made?** The mistakes I have made as an investor have come from ignoring my own advice. I bought Berkshire Hathaway when it was cheap—$900 a share— but I didn't buy with conviction and should have scooped up a lot more. It's now worth $82,800 a

14

share. I also got caught up a bit in the quest for Internet stock riches, even though my indicators told me that the market was overvalued.

●**You detailed those indicators in your book,** *Yes, You Can Time the Market*. **How do you use this strategy for retirement investing?** My definition of market timing bears no resemblance to that of most financial gurus. No one can consistently predict what will happen in the stock market within the next year or the next five, but you can identify when stocks are cheaper by historical standards. If you buy stocks in those periods, your likelihood of making money over 20 years or longer is far better than if you dollar cost average into stock investments year after year, as many advisers recommend.

●**Tell us more about your research.** I sifted through 100 years of stock market data and found four simple measurements, or "metrics," that indicate with uncanny consistency when the S&P 500 was over- or undervalued. They include the current inflation-adjusted average price of stocks in the index…the index's average price-to-earnings ratio based on the trailing 12 months…average dividend yield…and average price-to-book value. You can find current figures, along with historical returns, on my book's Web site, *www.yesyoucantimethemarket.com*.

Next, I compared each of these metrics to their own 15-year moving averages. The optimal time to buy is at market lows—when the dividend yield is above its moving average and the rest of the metrics are well below theirs. You avoid stocks when the situation reverses itself.

Following this strategy, you would have bought stocks in 15 out of 15 of the best years to invest since 1926 and would have avoided the worst 15 years.

●**What do you do during overpriced stock market cycles?** Stay invested in the stocks I own, but I use new money to buy bonds (or bond funds), REITs (or REIT funds) and shares in a money market fund.

●**What do your charts say now?** The broad stock market is moderately underpriced—add to equities.

Try Flipping Properties To Beef Up Your Retirement Income

William Bronchick, attorney and CEO, Legalwiz Publications, Aurora, CO. He is president of the Colorado Association of Real Estate Investors.

If you have free time, energy and initiative, you can turn quick profits by buying and then reselling real estate—a practice called "flipping." It's a great opportunity for seniors looking for income to supplement their retirement savings.

Traditional real estate investing requires both capital and time. If you buy a property, you might have to wait 25 years to realize the full return.

Flipping real estate, on the other hand, seeks to turn properties over in months or even weeks. It requires virtually no capital and the profits can be virtually instantaneous.

HOW TO FLIP

Depending on your skill, experience and how much money you have to invest, you can wear one of three hats…

●**Scout.** Scouts don't actually buy property. They locate deals and pass the information to investors who do the actual buying. As a scout, you'll receive a fee from the investor.

●**Dealer.** Dealers not only find properties, but sign purchase contracts with sellers. The aim is to close on the contract and sell the property—or just the contract—to another investor. As a dealer, your profit will come from the spread between the purchase and sale price.

●**Retailer.** Retailers actually buy the property—often from a dealer. The aim is to fix it up so it can be sold at a profit to an owner-occupant.

I pay my scouts from $500 to $1,500 for finding me deals. I am paid the same when I act as scout. As a dealer, I've made as much as $10,000 by flipping a property to a retailer.

LEARNING THE ROPES

When it comes to flipping, determination counts for more than experience or capital. Learn as much as you can about mortgages and deeds and how a real estate closing works. The practice of flipping can be learned from books, seminars and from actually going out and doing it. (My book, *Flipping Properties* [Dearborn Trade], covers the topic in just over 200 pages.)

Strategy: If you're short on capital and real estate experience, start as a scout, finding deals for other investors. Once you gain experience, contacts and capital, you might become a dealer. If you have a skill that could be useful in rehabilitating a property—maybe you were a plumber or electrical contractor—you could buy run-down properties, fix them up and sell them. Then you would be a retailer.

GETTING STARTED

Once you've learned the basics, jump in and start scouting properties. *Here's how to begin...*

•**Surround yourself with like-minded people.** Seek out real estate investors in your community. They know the ropes—and will buy the deals you scout for them.

There's a local chapter of the National Association of Real Estate Investors (NAREI) in every major city. Visit *www.narei.com* to find a chapter near you.

Each chapter consists of 200 or so real estate investors who meet once a month and talk about the deals they're doing. You'll meet rehabbers looking for properties to buy and dealers with properties to sell. If you want to flip real estate, this is the network you must become part of.

•**Talk only to motivated sellers.** That's the key to flipping—finding properties going at below-market prices because the owner is in a financial bind. By the time a property is in foreclosure, everyone knows about it. You want to find properties before they go into foreclosure.

Where to look: Run newspaper ads looking for distressed properties. Focus on a single neighborhood—send out postcards, use flyers and rent ad space on bus-stop benches.

If you follow that strategy, you'll need to spend some money on ads, business cards and the rest. Set an advertising budget (about $500, more in large cities), and consider it the cost of doing business.

If you would rather commit time than capital, look for deals by driving through your target neighborhood. Check out "for sale by owner" signs. If the property looks run down and in need of repair, phone the owner. Better still, pick up the newspaper and call everyone in that

neighborhood with a house for sale. You don't want to know about the house as much as you do about the seller's needs.

Ask each seller, "How quickly do you want to sell?" If the answer is, "When I get a good deal," they're not motivated. If the answer is, "As quickly as possible," you have a motivated seller. If you start Saturday morning, you'll have a fistful of leads by Sunday night.

•**Be persistent.** Few deals are made on the first try. Most deals won't be made until you've talked to the seller four or five times.

When you start out, be prepared to get one useful lead for each 100 properties you scout. When you get good, at least one lead in 20 that comes your way will be worth money.

HOW TO SELL

Approach the sales process backward—find the investor/buyer *before* finding the seller.

Strategy: Say you're working as a dealer, and you're looking for properties to flip to other investors. Line up your investors first. When you find what they're looking for, you already have the property flipped before you sign the contract to buy it. That's where your network among local real estate investors pays off, since they're the people who will buy the deals you turn up.

Of course, these investors could find dealers on their own. But it saves a lot of time and legwork if you can deliver the deals to them.

You Can Buy Real Estate With Your IRA

Patrick W. Rice, licensed real estate broker and investment manager for more than 25 years. His firm, IRA Resource Associates, in Camas, WA, purchases properties for its clients' IRAs, http://iraresource.com. He is coauthor of IRA Wealth: Revolutionary IRA Strategies for Real Estate Investment. Square One.

There's something your stockbroker won't tell you—you can purchase the retirement home of your dreams with your IRA.

Traditional and Roth IRAs can be used to purchase all kinds of property, from single-family homes to apartment buildings.

By owning real estate, you diversify away from stocks and bonds and keep ahead of inflation. Returns for real estate average 14% a year, versus the 12% 30-year average for stocks.*

Although banks and brokerage firms typically don't offer this alternative—it is costly to administer and does not generate trading commissions—it's easy to add a real estate strategy to your retirement plan.

Reasonable allocation now: 25% or more of your retirement assets.

Beware: If you buy a home for retirement, you can't live in it until you take its entire value as a distribution from your IRA after age 59½. Until then, rent it out to a permissible third party. Profits are reinvested in your IRA.

CASE STUDIES

•**Residential property.** Harry dreamed of retiring to Galveston, Texas, near his brother. He bought a house there using money in his IRA.

Purchase price: $120,000.

Expenses: $4,500/year for taxes, insurance, utilities, etc.

Net operating income: $7,500/year (annual rent of $12,000 less annual expenses of $4,500).

Annual income: 6.25% (net operating income divided by the purchase price). Assuming that the home appreciates in value by 6% a year, Harry ends up with a 12.25% annual return.

Harry achieved his goal by renting out the house until retirement and then taking the house as a distribution from his IRA. His tenants moved out. He moved in and became the new owner instead of his IRA.

•**Commercial property.** Steve's IRA purchased a building that housed a Pizza Hut restaurant in Malta, Montana. The tenant was three years into a 10-year lease with options to extend the lease for five years.

Purchase price: $325,000.

Expenses: Nominal. Utilities, taxes and insurance were paid by the tenant.

Net operating income: $30,000/year.

Annual income: 9.23%.

While Steve's income is at the low end of the average for commercial property (the range is 8% to 14% a year), Steve liked the security of the

*According to Ibbotson Associates, which used real estate investment trusts as a proxy for real estate.

long-term lease. The costs also were contained because the tenant was responsible for most expenses. Steve got the building for less than the $350,000 asking price because he agreed to pay cash and was able to close quickly. He still owns this building.

SET UP YOUR PROGRAM

Transfer your existing IRA or roll over money from a qualified plan—a 401(k) or a pension—to a special account called a *self-directed IRA.* It should be overseen by a custodian, such as a bank, which receives an annual fee of 0.5% to 1.5% of assets. Fees decline as assets increase.

My favorite custodians: Fiserv, 800-962-4238, *www.fiserviss.com*...PENSCO Trust Co., 800-969-4472, *www.pensco.com.*

You also will need a property manager to maintain and rent out the property to tenants. You are not legally permitted to manage it yourself because the IRS considers you a "disqualified party."

FINANCE YOUR PURCHASES

If you don't have enough cash in the IRA to buy a property outright, invest your money with others in a limited liability company (LLC). The LLC invests in the property. There are no restrictions on eligible investors. For instance, the LLC can buy the property with your IRA and/or your spouse's IRA as well as with non-retirement accounts belonging to you and your spouse.

WATCH OUT FOR TAX TRAPS

If you want to rent the property to family members, consult a tax attorney. If you violate IRS rules, you will pay tax on the entire investment. *IRS rules are tricky...*

•**You cannot lease the property to parties that have been disqualified by the IRS,** such as yourself, parents, children, spouse, grandchildren or their spouses. The law *does* allow you to lease the property to siblings, cousins, uncles and aunts. You also can name a sibling, etc., to manage the property. You pay that person a salary.

•**You cannot use IRA-owned property** as collateral for a home-equity loan or line of credit.

•**You cannot use non-IRA funds to pay** for expenses, such as insurance, taxes and repairs.

Exception: Legal fees. Make sure the property generates enough income to cover these costs. If necessary, you could transfer money from other IRAs to your self-directed IRA in order to cover expenses.

To keep legal fees down, only use an attorney to draw up and review documents, not to negotiate deals. It is best to pay legal fees with non-IRA money so that you can deduct the cost from your taxes.

•If you move into the property after age 59½, you must take it as a distribution from your IRA and pay tax based on the current value of the property. Plan for the tax—it could be sizable. If the property is in a Roth IRA, you pay no taxes.

CHOOSE YOUR INVESTMENTS

Base real estate decisions on the amount of time you're willing to commit, your risk tolerance and the size of your IRA.

•Residential property.

Who it is good for: Conservative investors who want to secure their dream home now or purchase a home for an investment.

How it works: Since you will have to hire a property manager to take care of the property anyway, there is no reason to limit your search to just your own neighborhood. Consider homes around the US.

•Commercial property.

Who it is good for: Investors who are willing to take more risk for higher capital appreciation.

How it works: You will need a commercial broker to help you select potential investments—stores, office buildings, hotels and land.

For referrals to real estate agents, contact the National Council of Exchangors, a nonprofit organization, 800-324-1031, *www.infoville.com.*

Hire a firm that handles a well-maintained property in the area to manage your commercial property.

Cost: 4% to 10% of the annual rent collected.

There are good buys on commercial properties all over the US now. I recently purchased properties in California, Kentucky, Missouri, New York and Washington.

Stop Uncle Sam From Stealing Your Retirement Dollars

Ed Slott, CPA, editor, *Ed Slott's IRA Advisor*, 100 Merrick Rd., Rockville Centre, NY 11570, *www.irahelp.com.* He is a nationally recognized IRA distributions expert.

From the moment you make your very first deposit in a traditional IRA or 401(k), you're building up a savings account—*for the IRS.*

Uncle Sam eventually gets a big chunk of your money. All withdrawals are taxable and at ordinary income tax rates of as high as 35%, not at the lower capital gains rate. If your retirement accounts and other assets grow to more than $2 million in 2006, your heirs will owe estate tax on traditional and Roth IRAs upon your death. *Five ways to protect your money…*

USE ROTH IRAS

This is Uncle Sam's greatest gift to retirement savings. Yet several years after the Roth's debut, relatively few people have taken advantage of it. Roth IRAs give no up-front tax deduction, but your money grows tax free. Roth IRA beneficiaries do not owe income tax on the distributions. A beneficiary can "stretch" the benefit, leaving the money to continue growing tax free over his/her life. *Here's what to do…*

•If you're planning to open a new IRA, make it a Roth. Your adjusted gross income (AGI) must be less than $110,000 (single) or $160,000 (married filing jointly).

•Convert a traditional IRA to a Roth. In this case, your AGI must not exceed $100,000, whether you are single or married filing jointly. You will have to pay tax on gains on the traditional IRA. Ask the financial institution that handles your IRA what your tax liability will be. If bear market losses have reduced the value of your IRA, you will owe less tax.

Note: Required minimum distributions from IRAs are no longer counted as part of your AGI for the $100,000 limit.

You can't roll over money from a 401(k) directly to a Roth. You must first roll it into a traditional IRA and then convert that to a Roth. Ask your tax adviser for advice.

Loophole: Your AGI only has to fall below $100,000 for one year to qualify for conversion. If your income is a few thousand dollars more than $100,000, shift some income to next year and/or sell stocks to take capital losses in taxable accounts. Losses also might put you in a lower bracket and reduce tax on the conversion.

Trap: Anyone who is married but files a separate return cannot convert a traditional IRA to a Roth, regardless of income.

HELP FUTURE GENERATIONS DODGE TAXES

When 401(k) or IRA assets pass to heirs, they in turn can stretch the tax shelter over their lives. *Examples...*

Example 1: A husband leaves an IRA to his wife. She names their children as her beneficiaries. After her death, her children can enjoy tax-free compounding on the amount remaining. In this manner, tax deferral could go on for many years.

Example 2: Your daughter is age 40 when she inherits your traditional IRA. According to IRS tables, a 40-year-old has a life expectancy of another 43.6 years. Despite taking *required minimum distributions* (RMDs), the account can continue to earn investment returns during this period.

WATCH OUT FOR WITHDRAWAL PENALTIES

Uncle Sam's 10% early withdrawal penalty applies to both Roth and traditional IRA withdrawals made before age 59½.

There is a 50% penalty if you fail to take RMDs on traditional IRAs. If your RMD is $20,000 and you miss the deadline, your penalty is $10,000. *What to do...*

•**Traditional IRAs.** Start taking RMDs by April 1 of the year after you turn 70½. The percentage you must withdraw each year is determined by the IRS from life expectancy tables. For more information, call 800-829-1040, or go to *www.irs.gov* or *www.irahelp.com*.

•**Roth IRAs.** There are no required distributions for Roth IRA owners.

Loophole: You can withdraw money without penalty from any IRA before age 59½ using one of three IRS formulas. But watch out—if you start spending your nest egg early, you might not have enough savings for retirement.

LET LIFE INSURANCE PAY YOUR TAXES

Employer-sponsored retirement plans—such as 401(k)s—and traditional and Roth IRAs count toward your estate, so purchase insurance to pay the estate tax.

Estate tax in 2006 can be as high as 46% for estates of more than $2 million. Income tax on distributions from traditional IRAs can be as high as 35%.

While the estate tax is supposed to vanish in 2010, it is scheduled to return in 2011. Base your planning on the tax as it is today, affecting estates that are bigger than $2 million.

If there is no estate tax, your heirs will get to keep the payout.

What to do: Assume that estate tax will be 50% of the value of assets—cars, homes, retirement plans, other investments, etc. Purchase enough life insurance to cover the potential tax. At your death, insurance proceeds are free from income tax.

Important: Create a life insurance trust to own the policy so that the value is kept out of your estate. You can name beneficiaries—your spouse or children—as trustees. Make annual gifts to beneficiaries, which they should use to pay the insurance premiums. You won't owe gift tax if the payments are no more than $12,000 per recipient per year ($24,000 if given by a couple). For information, consult an experienced trust attorney.

PROVIDE FOR BENEFICIARIES NOW

Whether you have a traditional or Roth IRA, you must name your beneficiary on a retirement plan beneficiary form, which takes legal precedence over your will.

If you don't take the right steps, a lengthy, expensive probate court process will determine who inherits your IRA.

Update beneficiary forms when there is a marriage or divorce, new child or grandchild or other change that would affect your choice of a beneficiary.

Keep beneficiary forms filed with other important papers as well as with your attorney and tax adviser. Then they can be located readily by family members and the executor of your will upon your death.

Tax Traps to Avoid In Retirement Plan Distributions

Ed Slott, CPA, editor, *Ed Slott's IRA Advisor*, 100 Merrick Rd., Rockville Centre, NY 11570, *www.irahelp.com*. He is a nationally recognized IRA distributions expert.

Tax-deferred retirement plans, such as IRAs and 401(k)s, enable you to build up a sizable nest egg. However, you need to be careful when taking distributions and naming beneficiaries. *Tax traps to avoid...*

WITHDRAWALS

Trap: Withdrawals before age 59½ usually trigger a 10% penalty.

Loophole: There are several exceptions to this penalty, permitting you or your heirs to take some cash from your plan before age 59½.

Examples: Disability, death.

Also, if you retire or change jobs, you can withdraw money from an employer-sponsored plan, penalty free, if the separation occurs during or after the year you turn age 55.

In addition, you can take substantially equal periodic payments (SEPPs), penalty free, for at least five years or until the age of 59½, whichever comes later.

Caution: The rules for SEPPs are complex, so you need to work with a savvy tax pro.

Trap: If you don't start to take required minimum distributions (RMDs) by April 1 of the year after you reach age 70½, you could face a 50% penalty.

Once you reach that age, you must withdraw the minimum amount each year and pay tax on it. As long as you're alive and there is money left in your account, you will be required to continue to take these minimum distributions.

You can choose to take larger distributions from your retirement account, if you wish, however you must withdraw at least the minimum amount each year.

Example: Suppose you are 76 years old and have $220,000 in your IRA. According to the IRS's Uniform Lifetime Table—found in Publication 590, *Individual Retirement Arrangements (IRAs)*, 800-829-3676 or *www.irs.gov*—you have a life expectancy of 22 more years. Thus, you must withdraw at least ¹⁄₂₂ of your IRA this year, or $10,000.

If, instead, you withdraw only $2,000, you have an $8,000 shortfall. As a result, you'll owe a $4,000 penalty, which is 50% of the $8,000 shortfall.

Again, calculating the minimum withdrawal can be complicated. Consult your tax adviser (don't rely on bank information).

Loophole: There are no lifetime RMDs for Roth IRAs. And you don't need to take required distributions at age 70½ if you're still working. That's true as long as you don't own more than 5% of your company. If you begin working after having started RMDs, you can discontinue RMDs from that company's plan, assuming the plan allows it. You still have to take RMDs from other plans and IRAs.

The exception applies only to withdrawals from employer-sponsored plans. If you roll your account balance to an IRA, the minimum distribution rules apply, even if you're still working.

Loophole: You can roll IRA money into an employer-sponsored plan if the plan will accept it.

Strategy: If you're working after age 70½ and you don't need to take distributions, roll your IRA into your employer's plan, if possible. You will forgo having to take distributions and avoid the 50% penalty.

SAFE BUT SORRY

In order to avoid the 50% penalty, you might take out more money than you really need.

Example: Before you reach age 79, your required distribution will be less than 5% per year. Thus, if you withdraw 5% of your balance each year, you'll avoid a penalty.

Trap: Taking 5% per year from your retirement plan is fine if you need the money. However, if you currently don't need income and you withdraw more than the minimum, you'll pay more income tax than you need to pay and sooner than you need to pay it. More important, excess withdrawals reduce the amount of tax-deferred wealth-building that you (and possibly your beneficiaries) can enjoy.

If you do not need the money for living expenses, withdraw only the bare minimum.

NAMING BENEFICIARIES

Trap: If you don't name a beneficiary, whoever inherits your account will have to withdraw more money sooner and pay more income tax. The same is true if you name your estate as the beneficiary.

Strategy: Name one or more individuals as beneficiaries on the form provided by the custodian or on a custom form you provide.

If you have doubts about your beneficiary's ability to handle a large inheritance, name a trust as the beneficiary, then name your heirs as trust beneficiaries.

Loophole: If handled properly, setting up such a trust can permit your heirs to stretch out required withdrawals. Work with an experienced trust attorney.

COMPANY STOCK

If you work for a publicly traded company, chances are that your retirement plan account contains some company stock.

Trap: Mishandling the withdrawal of that stock could cost you a prime tax break.

Example: Your 401(k) is $200,000, including $50,000 of company stock. When you retire, you roll over the entire $200,000 to an IRA. All subsequent IRA withdrawals will be subject to ordinary income tax, at rates up to 35%.

Strategy: Before you execute the rollover, ask about your basis in the company stock. That's the amount it was worth when the shares were contributed to your retirement account.

Loophole: You can pull out those shares and pay tax only on your basis, and not on their current value.

Example: Say your company shares are now worth $50,000 but your basis in those shares is only $10,000. You could withdraw the $50,000 worth of shares but owe tax on only $10,000 worth of income.

The other $40,000 won't be taxed until you sell the shares, which might be right away or many years in the future. In the meantime, you can receive dividends from all the shares and you can borrow against them, if you wish.

Result: Whenever you decide to sell the shares, the $40,000 will be taxed as a long-term capital gain, at a top tax rate of 15% under current law instead of at ordinary income tax rates of up to 35% on regular IRA withdrawals. After more than one year, any additional gains also will qualify for the bargain tax rate.

The remaining assets in your 401(k) can be rolled into an IRA, tax free. You won't pay income tax until you begin making withdrawals.

Shrewd Tax Planning for Mutual Fund Investors

Dennis A. Ito, partner in charge, personal financial planning, Western Area, and Rande Spiegelman, manager of personal financial planning, KPMG, LLP, 3 Embarcadero Center, Suite 2000, San Francisco 94111.

Tax planning can help you keep more of what your mutual funds return. And recent changes in the tax rules for capital gains make it even *more* important to identify which funds are best for different accounts.

YOUR GOALS

Mutual fund investments are taxed at two levels…

• **You, the investor, face a capital gain**—or loss—when you sell your shares in a mutual fund.

• **The mutual fund *itself* realizes taxable investment income** in the form of the capital gains, dividends and interest it earns during the year. This income is distributed to its shareholders through a dividend paid before year-end.

Trap: Fund shareholders *owe the tax* on these gains—a fact that they often overlook in their planning. If a fund reports high investment gains and the gains are subject to high tax rates, your after-tax return from the fund will be *lower* than it appears.

Your two tax goals as a fund investor should be to…

• **Manage your own shareholdings** to minimize capital gains tax due on them.

• **Select funds for your portfolio** that are tax efficient, meaning portfolio turnover is low.

Payoff: With smart planning, just one percentage point added to your *after-tax* investment returns will compound over time to significantly increase future wealth.

MINIMIZE CAPITAL GAINS

Gains are taxed depending on how long you hold the investment…

• **Short-term gains,** on assets held one year or less, are taxed at ordinary rates of up to 35%.

• **Long-term gains,** on assets held more than one year, are taxed at a top rate of only 15% —5% if you are in the 10% or 15% tax bracket.

You may own shares in a fund that you've purchased at different times and prices—giving you different amounts of gain and holding periods. If you sell *some* shares, you need a way to determine the amount and nature of your gain.

The IRS allows you to select from among four different methods of determining gain from the sale of mutual fund shares (see IRS Publication 564, *Mutual Fund Distributions*).

●**First-in, first-out (FIFO)** accounting treats your shares as being sold in the order in which you acquired them. The IRS presumes the use of FIFO unless you elect one of the other three methods.

●**Average cost method** computes your gain on a sale using the average cost of all the shares you own. Most mutual funds will compute this number for you, saving you work. However, this method often fails to produce the best possible tax result.

●**Average cost double category method** is rarely used. It allocates shares to long- and short-term holding periods according to the overall ratio of such holdings.

●**Specific share method** lets you select particular shares from among your holdings for sale.

Best option in most cases: The *specific share* method. It lets you choose among all your shares and select for sale the particular ones that produce the best tax result.

●You can sell your highest-cost shares to minimize taxable gain.

●If you have a capital loss elsewhere, you can sell your lowest-cost shares to maximize gain and use the loss to offset the gain from tax.

●You may even be able to generate a deductible loss when you've made a big profit on your shares overall.

The snag with the specific cost method is that you must have cost records for every share you own. And…when you sell shares, you must notify the fund in *writing* that you are using the method to identify the shares you are selling and their cost and receive written confirmation of your instructions.

Self-defense: From the day you set up your account with a fund, keep all the account records that the fund provides you, including trade confirmations and year-end statements.

Choose the best accounting method for you from the beginning. Once you use one of the four methods for a particular fund, you can't change it without IRS approval.

Dividend shares trap: Pay special attention to record keeping for shares acquired with reinvested dividends. These shares are taxed when you receive them and increase the cost basis of your total holdings. But many people forget to increase their tax basis to account for reinvested distributions and pay tax on the shares again when they sell them.

CUTTING TAXES

You control the taxable capital gains you report, but not the amount of taxable dividend income a mutual fund will distribute to you. So it's important to consider this income and the effect it has on a fund's total return.

Fund selection strategy: First look for funds that will meet your real investment needs. Then, among those, invest in the funds that have the lowest tax cost.

Beware: The most actively traded funds generally produce the largest taxable distributions—including short-term gains taxed at rates as high as 35%.

Contrast: Index funds that don't trade at all produce the smallest taxable distributions—near zero.

Some funds seek to trade "tax efficiently" by offsetting gains with losses and holding investments long enough to qualify as "long term."

Before buying a fund, study its prospectus for its trading philosophy and the record of gains it has produced.

Caution: Its pattern of performance may change, unless its prospectus states otherwise.

Helpful: Consider holding funds that produce taxable distributions in tax-favored retirement accounts, such as Roth IRAs and 401(k) plans, while holding tax-efficient funds in taxable accounts.

Trap: If you buy a fund and the market falls from a high level, the fund may distribute taxable gains to you even as you take a loss on your investment.

How that happens: As the value of your shares falls, the fund will be cashing in its appreciated gains to pay redemptions—and its gains will be taxed to you as a shareholder.

Some major fund groups are now making provisions against this event—so ask before investing.

Very Valuable Tax Deductions

Mary Wilson, CPA, JD, senior tax manager, Rothstein Kass, an international accounting and consulting firm in Roseland, NJ. *www.rkco.com.*

Many taxpayers don't take common deductions—for mortgage interest, charitable donations and medical expenses. The reason? They don't "itemize" by claiming these or any other expenses on Schedule A of Form 1040.

It's easy to see why. For many people, the standard deduction for 2005—$10,000 for couples filing jointly…$5,000 for single taxpayers —is higher than the total of their itemized deductions, so they're better off taking the standard deduction. In 2006, the standard deduction is even higher—$10,300 for couples and $5,150 for singles.

There are several smart ways to boost your tax savings even if you don't itemize and instead take the standard deduction. A number of so-called *above-the-line* write-offs are available. *Common examples…*

INDIVIDUAL RETIREMENT ACCOUNTS (IRAS)

In 2006, you can contribute up to $4,000 to an IRA ($5,000 for those age 50 and older). *Roth IRA contributions are never tax-deductible, but there are situations in which you can deduct contributions to a traditional IRA…*

●**If you are not covered by an employer-sponsored retirement plan.**

●**If your income is under certain thresholds,** even if you are covered by an employer-sponsored retirement plan. Single filers must have incomes of less than $50,000 in 2006 to be eligible for a full IRA write-off. Lesser deductions are available for those with incomes up to $60,000. For joint filers, the limits are $75,000 and $85,000, respectively, in 2006.

●**If your joint income is less than $150,000 and only one spouse works.** The nonworking spouse can take this deduction even if the working spouse is covered by an employer-sponsored retirement plan.

HEALTH SAVINGS ACCOUNTS (HSAs)

HSAs, created under the 2003 Medicare drug law, became effective in 2004.

How HSAs work: They are IRA-like accounts that can be used to pay health-care expenses.

Contributions: To deduct your contributions to an HSA, you must be covered by a high-deductible health plan and not covered by Medicare. In 2006, the annual deductible on health insurance must be at least $1,050 ($2,100 for joint filers).

You can contribute up to the amount of your policy's deductible, to a maximum set by the IRS.

Example: With a $1,200 deductible, you can put as much as $1,200 per year into an HSA.

If you are age 55 or older by the end of 2006, you can contribute $700 *more* than the policy deductible. The maximum HSA contribution for 2006 is $2,700…or $5,450 for those with family coverage. If you have an HSA, you still can contribute to an IRA, a 401(k) and a flexible spending account at work.

Withdrawals: Withdrawals can be made tax free from the HSA to pay medical bills. Unused HSA money can be carried over to subsequent years to grow tax deferred through investments in mutual funds, stocks, bonds, etc.—potentially for decades. Money withdrawn before age 65 that is not used for health-related purposes is subject to income tax and a 10% penalty. After age 65, you pay only income tax.

STUDENT-LOAN INTEREST

You can deduct up to $2,500 worth of interest paid on student loans this year, regardless of how many students there are in the family and whether the loan financed higher education for you, your spouse and/or a dependent, provided your income is below a set amount.

LEGAL FEES IN DISCRIMINATION SUITS

If you recover an award in a discrimination action (the full amount of which is taxable income), legal fees are deductible even if you do not itemize.

ALIMONY

Alimony is 100% deductible for the payer and is considered taxable income for the recipient. If you're the payer, you'll have to provide your former spouse's Social Security number on your return so that the IRS can check on the resulting tax collection.

MOVING EXPENSES

If you move because of a new job or for other business reasons, certain expenses are deductible—costs to transport household goods and personal effects as well as your travel to the new residence. This includes lodging but not meals. To qualify, your new workplace must be more than 50 miles farther from your old home than your former workplace was from your old home.

EARLY WITHDRAWAL PENALTIES

If you cash in a bank CD, any resulting penalty can be deducted.

SPECIAL WRITE-OFFS
FOR THE SELF-EMPLOYED

•**Self-employment retirement plans.** If you have self-employment income, even from a sideline business, several types of retirement plans are available, among them SEP, SIMPLE, individual 401(k) and Keogh plans. Contributions to these plans are deductible regardless of whether you itemize. For rules on deducting these contributions, see IRS Publication 560, *Retirement Plans for Small Business*, available by calling 800-TAX-FORM or visiting *www.irs.gov*.

•**Self-employment tax.** The bad news is that self-employed individuals must pay both the employer's and the employee's share of Medicare and Social Security taxes. The good news is that you can deduct half of those payments even if you don't itemize.

•**Self-employment health insurance.** You can deduct 100% of health insurance premiums that you pay for yourself, your spouse and your dependents. The amount you deduct can't exceed your self-employment income.

What the IRS Won't Tell You About Audits

Frederick W. Daily, tax attorney, 741 Tyler Way, Incline Village, NV 85451. He is author of *Stand Up to the IRS* and *Tax Savvy for Small Business* (both from Nolo Press).

Most taxpayers who face an IRS auditor fear how much the IRS knows about them. Auditors use this fear to intimidate taxpayers into making concessions and revealing more.

With the right tactics, you can keep the IRS auditor from learning any more…and help move the audit to its best possible conclusion.

WHAT THE IRS KNOWS

When you appear for an IRS audit, the auditor will have a file on your case that typically contains only three sources of information about you…

•**Tax return being audited.**

•**Your tax-filing history for the past six years.** This tells whether you filed tax returns …were audited…or had a tax bill adjusted for those years. It does *not* include copies of prior years' tax returns.

•**List of third-party payments made to you** that were reported to the IRS on W-2 and 1099 forms or other information returns.

In 90% of cases, that's all the information the auditor will have about you before the audit begins.

If information that could cause you audit problems is not contained among these three items, the overwhelming odds are that the auditor doesn't have it.

Then the only way the auditor can get it is from you or by issuing a summons on the record keeper.

The auditor will not have: Copies of bank statements, motor vehicle records, property deeds or police records. Nor will he/she have copies of 1099s or other information returns sent to the IRS under a Social Security or taxpayer ID number other than yours.

Key: Don't volunteer any information to the IRS auditor that you aren't legally obligated to give —even if he asks for it.

THE BIGGEST MISTAKE

By far the most common audit mistake is providing copies of your other years' tax returns just because the audit notice asks you to do so.

Doing so greatly expands audit risk by giving the auditor many things to look at that he otherwise would not see.

Patterns of income and deduction amounts reported over multiple years may raise questions that would not arise when looking at just a single year's return.

The fact that an auditor doesn't have information doesn't mean he won't ask for it. So it's important to know what you are legally required to provide to an auditor…and what you aren't.

Rule: You are required to provide an IRS auditor only the information relating to the specific tax year listed in the audit notice. You are not required to provide information relating to any other tax year, except as it might relate to the year under audit—as carryover items might.

SAYING NO

Most people never imagine saying no to an IRS auditor for fear that the auditor might retaliate by expanding the audit.

This fear is greatly exaggerated—retaliation is unlikely. IRS auditors have no incentive to expand an audit. They are evaluated by how quickly they close cases and work through their caseloads. And those caseloads are very heavy.

Inside secret: An auditor who feels there is good reason to examine another year's tax return can obtain it from the IRS's own files, but it may take weeks or months for the IRS to retrieve that old return. One who doesn't take the trouble to do so probably is "just fishing" for the taxpayer to reveal something.

The way to say *no* safely to such an auditor is to respond politely, "I don't believe that this relates to the year or issues being examined." Almost always, that will end the matter.

THE RIGHT REPRESENTATION

If there is information you want to protect from the IRS, consider being represented at your audit by a tax professional—instead of attending the audit personally. They are experienced at dealing with auditors.

A professional representative will not have the answers to some of the auditor's questions

—including any information that you might reveal unintentionally.

Your representative will ask the auditor to put the request in writing. Then, in responding to a written request, your representative can discuss things with you and draft as narrow an answer as possible.

The whole process will slow the audit, which the auditor doesn't want. So attempts by the auditor to "go fishing" will be frustrated.

The IRS cannot conduct a "lifestyle or economic reality audit," asking questions that are unrelated to the preparation of the return being examined, unless it already has a reasonable indication that income has been understated.

A professional representative will also prevent your emotions or personal factors from complicating an audit. No matter how difficult the audit may be, your representative should be able to deal with the auditor in a calm and professional manner.

The fee you pay may be a bargain for both the taxes it saves and the anxiety you avoid by not dealing with the auditor personally.

And, last but not least, fees paid to a tax professional for defending an audit are deductible.

Minimizing Chances Of a Tax Audit

To be candid, there is no way of being sure that your federal income tax return won't be audited. Even overpaying won't protect you from IRS scrutiny. Some returns are pulled out by random selection. Others are chosen by IRS computers, which analyze returns to score the likelihood of collecting further. Computers select a return for audit if medical expenses, contributions, property taxes, etc., represent an unusually high percentage of the taxpayer's income (according to nationwide experience). Returns also invite scrutiny when figures do not agree with other information received by the IRS, such as when a corporation reports on Form 1099 that it paid $2,000 in dividends to a taxpayer, but that taxpayer reports only $1,000. And returns also may be selected for audit because of tips provided by tax informants.

But your chances of being audited can be reduced greatly by following these suggestions...

●**Answer *all* questions on the tax return form.**

●**Complete all schedules that are required.** Use the words *"None"* or *"Not applicable"* where appropriate.

●**Include full documentation of items that are certain to be questioned,** such as large casualty losses or large moving expenses. If the IRS asks for unsupplied substantiation, expect this request to lead to additional questions in other areas of the return at the same time.

●**Send tax returns and other documents to the right office** at the right time so that correspondence and personal contact aren't necessary. Once begun, such correspondence or contact is often difficult to end—one thing leads to another.

●**Don't deduct a type of item that had been disallowed** on a previous tax return. The IRS may remember this and look for a repeat.

●**Don't use a tax preparer of dubious character.** If the IRS, through its investigators, finds a preparer who is grossly incompetent or *worse*, the names of all his/her clients will be obtained. All of them, however innocent, will have their tax returns checked by experts.

●**Be certain that the return has the right signatures and identifying numbers.** If it is a corporate return, the title of the signer should be one of the officers *authorized by law* to sign.

Many audits are triggered by...

●**Information returns from banks,** investments or employers that show payments (dividends, interest, salaries or fees) that differ from those that were reported.

●**Unusually large deductions.** The computer flags deductions that are much larger than the average amount taken by most taxpayers in the same income group.

Suggestions: Provide some details on extra-large deductions. Big casualty loss? Describe the hurricane or flood, maybe even enclose a newspaper clipping. Give dates and details of a long illness or a serious accident that produced large medical deductions.

●**Unbelievable numbers.**

Examples: Claiming that you held real estate or IBM stock for 25 years and sold it at a loss...Large deductions and losses that leave no money to live on...Business expenses that are out of line with the amount of gross income or the nature of the business...Mortgage interest and property tax deductions that are unusual for your area.

●**Large round numbers raise questions** as to whether you picked an exaggerated number out of the air without supporting documentation.

●**Office at home.** This set-up usually receives closer scrutiny.

Important: If the IRS strikes gold in auditing a return, it will often go after other members of the family, or partners, employees and other stockholders in the same S corporation.

Shrewd Ways to Use Your Home as a Tax Shelter

Diane Kennedy, CPA, a tax strategist for more than 20 years, D. Kennedy & Associates, certified public accountants, Phoenix. She is coauthor of several books, including *Real Estate Loopholes: Secrets of Successful Real Estate Investing.* Warner Business.

From a tax perspective, there's never been a better time to own a home. *Here are four loopholes to take advantage of...*

SHORT-TERM OWNERSHIP

The home-sale exclusion is one of the most generous tax breaks in the Internal Revenue Code. Married couples can avoid tax on up to $500,000 in capital gains ($250,000 for a single person). This break can be used over and over.

To get it, you must have owned the home and used it as your principal residence for at least two of the five years before the sale. Most people, however, don't realize how easy it is to use the exclusion even if you don't meet this two-year test.

Loophole: If you had to move out of a house before the two years were up because of an "unforeseen circumstance," you still can get a partial tax break. Unforeseen circumstances are defined liberally. They include natural disasters, a change in employment or becoming self-employed, divorce or legal separation, and multiple births from the same pregnancy.

How it works: Say you are promoted—or even demoted—at work. This is considered a change in employment, so you can sell your house and take a partial tax break even if you don't satisfy the two-year test. The same is true if you start, change or discontinue a business.

Example: You want to move from an appreciated property in which you have lived for less than two years. Before selling, you start a simple home-based business. Assuming that you sell the house after living in it for one year, you would get half of the maximum tax break because one year is half of two. You and your spouse could exclude up to $250,000 (half of $500,000) of any gain on the sale. A single filer could exclude up to $125,000 (half of $250,000).

HOME-OFFICE DEDUCTION

Some people don't deduct depreciation for a home office because they think it will cause them to owe tax on the gain allocated to the office when they sell the home. This is not the case.

Loophole: As long as the home office is part of your house—and not a separate structure—you will get the full principal-residence capital gains exclusion.

How it works: If you have taken a depreciation deduction for the office portion of your residence, you need to "recapture" the depreciation when you sell the home.

Example: If you have taken $10,000 of depreciation and are in the 25% bracket, you would owe $2,500 in tax—25% of $10,000—when you sell the home. You can keep whatever is left of the $500,000 or $250,000 exclusion on gains.

Paying less tax now (by depreciating) is worth more than the cost of recapturing depreciation later. For rules on depreciation, see IRS Publication 946, *How to Depreciate Property*, available at *www.irs.gov* or by calling 800-829-1040.

ASSET PROTECTION

In these litigious times, it's easy to imagine someone tripping on your driveway and suing you, putting your home and other assets at risk.

Strategy: To protect your home from creditors, transfer it to a single-member limited liability company (LLC). This isn't necessary if you live in states with "unlimited homestead protection"—

where equity is protected—such as Texas and Florida.

Loophole: Home owners who make such transfers still will be entitled to the mortgage interest deduction and capital gains exclusion. There can be only one owner, perhaps you and your spouse holding the title as joint tenants. You don't need to file an additional business tax return for the LLC.

DIVIDE AND CONQUER

You may be able to sell part of your property at a profit and still get the benefit of the capital gains exclusion.

Example: Your home sits on 40 acres. A developer buys 39 acres, from which you make a $300,000 profit. A year later, you sell the house and the remaining acre for an additional $150,000 profit.

Loophole: According to the Treasury Department, you can take the full $500,000 or $250,000 capital gains exclusion on the combined gain if you complete the "split sale" within two years.

In the above example, the total $450,000 gain ($300,000 plus $150,000) would be tax free, provided the house was sold within two years of the prior sale of the land and all other conditions were met.

Mortgage Payments Can Now Be Deducted on a Home You Don't Own

Saffet Uslu, TC Memo 1997-551.

A Tax Court decision shows how to save a mortgage interest deduction when one family member helps another obtain a home and mortgage payments are not made by the person whose name is on the mortgage.

Facts: A married couple found that they could not obtain a mortgage on the home they wanted to buy. The husband's brother then bought the home and let the couple live in it. The couple made all the mortgage payments on the house, even though both the mortgage and title to the home were in the brother's name.

The couple also paid all other ownership-related expenses, such as property taxes, utilities and so on, and acted in all ways as the owners of the home.

But when they tried to deduct the mortgage interest they paid, the IRS disallowed the deduction because they weren't legally obligated to pay the mortgage.

Tax Court: The couple were legally obligated to pay the mortgage because if they failed to do so, the brother would have a cause of action to evict them, and they would lose the home.

Because they had assumed all the rights and obligations of home ownership, and the brother hadn't taken the mortgage deduction, they could take the deduction.

---

14 Easy Ways to Boost The Value of Your Home

Jim Fite, president of Dallas-based Century 21 Judge Fite Company, one of the largest Century 21 affiliates in the world with more than $800 million in annual sales and more than 600 associates, *www.century21judgefite.com.*

Never underestimate the power of a good first impression. A home that looks attractive from the road can sell quickly, making it less likely that you'll have to reduce the asking price.

LANDSCAPE

1. Edge lawns and flowerbeds. A sharp edge gives a well-maintained look. Conversely, grass or weeds that are sprouting from cracks in paths implies neglect.

2. Add color. Plant flowers to make the front of a house come alive, particularly if the home itself is white or a dark color.

3. Patch cracks in walkways and sidewalks, even if the sidewalk is the town's responsibility. If tree roots have shattered a section, consider rerouting the sidewalk around the tree. Also, sweep all walks.

4. Trim overgrown trees and shrubs. Remove dead or dying plants.

HOUSE FACADE

5. Polish the doorknob. If the main entryway's doorknob or knocker shows signs of age, it's worth spending $150 or so to replace it.

6. Remove potted plants, statues and decorations from the front stoop. They make it look cluttered and smaller.

7. Use similar drapes in front windows. Most homeowners select drapes and blinds for the way they look inside the home—but different colors and shapes in front windows make a home look unbalanced from the outside.

8. Replace broken and missing shingles. Just a few bad shingles give the impression of roof problems—a big turnoff for potential buyers.

OTHER DETAILS

9. Remove weathered basketball hoops. Only keep them up if they look new and have nets.

10. Match your mailbox with your home. A cutesy mailbox is appropriate for a cutesy home. A $500,000 home shouldn't have a $10 mailbox.

11. Take down a dilapidated backyard fence, especially if it can be seen from someone standing in the street or driveway.

12. Remove decorative elements that could be considered clutter. Walkway lights and garden fountains are fine. Garden gnomes, out-of-season Christmas lights and other ornamentation should be packed away.

13. Keep garage doors closed. Even tidy garage interiors don't look as neat as closed garage doors. Garbage cans, rakes, bikes, etc., should be stored inside.

14. Maintain the "for sale" sign. A post that is leaning or in need of painting implies your home has been on the market for a long time. That suggests problems.

To Sell Your Home More Quickly...

Make your home more salable by paying attention to small details...

•**Take out the trash before prospective buyers visit.** If odors remain, bake bread or boil cinnamon to create a pleasant aroma.

•**Use higher-wattage bulbs** to make the house look brighter.

•**Make closets seem larger** by storing some of your clothes elsewhere temporarily.

•**If you have a cat,** be sure the litter box is clean and hidden.

Barbara Corcoran, chairman and founder, Corcoran Group, real estate brokerage firm, New York City, *www. barbaracorcoran.com.*

You Don't Need a Lot Of Money to Make Big Money in Real Estate

Carleton Sheets, real estate entrepreneur and author of *Real Estate: The World's Greatest Wealth Builder.* Bonus. He created the training program "How to Buy Your First Home or Investment Property with No Down Payment." 800-353-5219. *www.carletonsheets.com.*

The days of small-time investors making a killing in real estate are over. Home prices in such hot markets as Boston and San Francisco have nearly tripled since 1999. Going forward, rising inflation and a strengthening economy will cause mortgage rates to climb, eroding profits on real estate investments until rents have a chance to catch up. The Federal Reserve predicts that US housing prices over the next two years will grow at the slowest pace in more than three decades.

Despite these trends, one real estate strategy will excel—buying and renting out single-family homes. You don't have to be wealthy to be a successful landlord. You can use the equity in your existing home to get started, and you may qualify for generous tax breaks.

Owning one or two rental properties takes less time—and is less risky—than managing a stock portfolio, and there's always an up-and-coming real estate market waiting to be discovered.

Reality check: Owning rental property is a classic get-rich-*slow* strategy. Rental income covers the mortgage payments and operating expenses while providing a small positive cash flow.

However, you can increase the rent to keep up with or outpace inflation over the long term. You also can expect a profit when you sell—historically, home values have appreciated by about 5% a year, which is above and beyond the rental income.

How you can make money in single-family properties...

THE RIGHT KIND OF HOUSE

•**Look within a 20-mile radius of where you live.** You'll be better able to figure out the value of real estate in a familiar area. Unless you live in a hot market, you should be able to find affordable properties in your town.

If you can't afford to buy property in your town, expand your radius to 50 miles. Look for middle-income neighborhoods—homes in these neighborhoods stand the best chance of appreciating.

•**Buy sought-after properties.** Single-family homes with three bedrooms and two bathrooms appeal to a range of tenants. Avoid houses with only one or two bedrooms—they may be less expensive, but they are harder to rent or sell.

Also avoid condominiums and co-ops—you lack control. The building association may have the right to approve tenants. For example, applicants may be turned down if they have pets.

•**Look for popular features.** Choose a house that has at least one of the features that renters want—fenced-in yard...garage...fireplace...central air-conditioning...finished basement...or proximity to good schools, public transportation and supermarkets/shopping districts.

THE RIGHT DEAL

To ensure that the price is right, look up sales of comparable properties. *My favorite resources for valuing property...*

•**Recorder's office** at your county courthouse has records of a home's past and current owners and sale prices.

•**Tax assessor's office** has information on a property's assessed value, square footage, improvements, etc.

You also may find this information online—*www.statelocalgov.net* has links to municipal sites for all states.

•**DataQuick.com** (888-604-3282) provides reports on comparable sales, local crime rates, neighborhood demographics and real estate market trends.

Cost: $5 to $10 per report.

Make sure you will profit from the investment. A rental property should generate monthly income of at least 1% of the purchase price.

29

Example: I was interested in a house in an area where rents were about $900 per month. Therefore, I knew I could pay up to $90,000 for the house ($900 is 1% of $90,000). Even after I subtracted my projected expenses, including mortgage payments, maintenance, property taxes and insurance, I was left with cash flow of $100 a month.

TURNAROUND OPPORTUNITIES

Consider deeply discounted properties as you become more experienced. *They are likely to need work and may entail complex legal issues…*

●**Real estate owned (REO) properties.** Banks and institutional lenders are anxious to sell these foreclosed properties. Ask to see the REO lists at local banks. Try my site, *www.bank foreclosurelist.com*, to view more than 40,000 REO properties around the country.

●**Government-auctioned property.** Contact Housing and Urban Development, 202-708-1112, *www.hud.gov*…or Department of the Treasury, 202-622-2000, *www.treas.gov/auctions*, for information on auctions of federally owned properties.

FINANCING OPTIONS

Try to get financing from the seller. You'll be able to make a lower down payment than if you finance with a bank. In today's rental market, I find that as much as 15% of sellers are willing and able to finance purchases.

The seller acts like a bank, allowing you to use the property as collateral. You issue the seller a note with an agreed-upon interest rate (similar to the prevailing bank rate), then make mortgage payments directly to him/her.

If you default on your payments, the seller can foreclose on the property. As with any real estate deal, you should use an attorney or title company to assist with the closing.

Many sellers want extra assurances that you will make your mortgage payments. *Here's what you can offer…*

●**Earmark part of the rent you collect toward your principal.**

Example: When a student from my real estate seminar wanted to buy a residential property in Florida, the seller was willing to finance the $180,000 purchase but wanted 10% up front. The student only had $10,000. To close the deal, he gave the seller preference on the property's cash flow—the first

$500 in rent each month—until the additional $8,000 was collected.

●**Put up more collateral than the property is worth.** This is known as a "blanket mortgage."

Example: Another student found a rental house that was selling for $480,000. The student already owned other property, and he had no cash for a down payment. So he offered additional collateral—a property he owned in Vermont that was worth $60,000 and his personal residence in which he had $40,000 worth of equity. In lieu of a down payment, he put up $580,000 in collateral for the $480,000 house.

Important: Use a blanket mortgage only if you are absolutely confident that you can make your mortgage payments.

MANAGING
THE PROPERTY

●**Hire a management company if you don't want to maintain the property yourself.**

Typical cost: Half of one month's rent for finding and screening tenants…10% of the gross monthly rent for managing the property. Factor this in when you assess the net income of a prospective purchase. Ask for referrals from landlords in the area.

●**Run a credit and criminal check on prospective tenants.** Ask for references from employers and past landlords. Companies such as Intelius (425-974-6100, *http://find.intelius.com*) can run background checks for a fee.

●**Reward renters for prompt payments.** I charge rent that is 5% to 10% higher than the going rate, then offer that amount as a rental discount if the tenant pays on time.

●**Charge more than the monthly rent for the security deposit.** Otherwise, tenants may skip the last month's rent and tell you to use the deposit instead.

●**Keep two months' rental income in reserve** to protect against vacancies.

●**Make sure you have adequate property and liability coverage.** Consult an agent who has insured rental properties. *Helpful resources…*

●Landlord.com (408-374-9400) provides free forms, such as lease agreements, and online calculators.

•National Association of Independent Landlords (800-352-3395, *www.nail-usa.com*) has links to state laws.

Dangers of Cosigning A Loan

You will be listed with credit bureaus as responsible for the loan—and your credit could be damaged if payments are missed. Since the amount of the loan appears as your debt, you may find it harder to qualify for a loan of your own. If payment trouble develops, you may not find out until the borrower has defaulted and your credit has been damaged.

Extra danger: Cosigning on credit cards. Since credit lines may be increased periodically, you may end up being responsible for much more than you planned.

Gerri Detweiler, credit specialist, Sarasota, FL, and author of *Invest In Yourself.* John Wiley & Sons.

A Great Business You Can Start In Your Home

Stephen Wagner, author of *Mind Your Own Business: The Best Businesses You Can Start Today for Under $500.* Adams Media.

You can start a credit-repair service out of your home with a minimal investment. Customers usually seek this service after being rejected for a home or car loan. You would resolve their credit disputes, set up payment schedules with credit card companies, etc.

Key: Screen potential clients. You want those you can actually help. To be eligible for your services, problem accounts must have been paid off for at least one year, preferably three or four. Guarantee clients an overall improvement in their credit.

The only cost to you is for office expenses, placement of ads in area newspapers, research of credit record keeping and reporting laws.

Earning potential: $100,000 a year.

CONFIDENTIAL REPORT #2:

The Doctor's Handbook of Healing Remedies and Medical Breakthroughs

The Doctor's Handbook of Healing Remedies and Medical Breakthroughs

Cut Your Risk of Cancer By Two-Thirds by Just Eating Wisely

Can changing your diet eliminate your risk of developing cancer? That proposition—the centerpiece of a book called *The Breast Cancer Prevention Diet* (Little, Brown)—caused a firestorm of controversy when it was first published.

Critics of the book, written by television correspondent Bob Arnot, MD, argue that nothing can eliminate the danger of cancer altogether. They're right. No diet, supplement or drug can *guarantee* you won't get cancer. But you *can* do a great deal to protect yourself.

Diet is now believed to be a factor in approximately 60% of all malignancies—with smoking, heredity and viral infections accounting for the rest of them.

Theoretically, an effective anticancer diet should be capable of cutting your cancer risk by approximately two-thirds.

NO QUICK FIX

The most compelling demonstrations of cancer risk reduction come from *population studies*. These experiments compare the incidence of certain diseases among different groups of people. Among other things, these studies show that cancer rates are much lower in developing nations than in the US.

Citizens of developing nations tend to eat *very* differently than the average American. The average American eats lots of fatty and/or highly processed foods. In developing countries, people eat mostly fruits, vegetables and grains.

WHAT TO AVOID

It's now well established that eating less dietary fat can cut your cancer risk. Dietary fat clearly raises the risk for breast, colon and prostate cancers.

In addition, you must avoid foods known to raise cancer risk—and boost consumption of foods that lower the risk...

J. Robert Hatherill, PhD, research scientist, environmental studies program, University of California in Santa Barbara. He is author of *Eat to Beat Cancer*. Renaissance.

35

•**Minimize consumption of beef, pork, poultry and fish.** These foods can be concentrated sources of dioxin, polychlorinated biphenyls (PCBs) and other potent carcinogens.

These compounds sap the body's cancer-fighting ability…and trigger genetic mutations that can lead to cancer.

•**Wash produce thoroughly.** If peeling is not an option, use VegiWash or another produce wash. Whenever possible, buy organic.

•**Drink more water.** Drinking eight eight-ounce glasses of water a day helps flush carcinogens out of the body.

•**Consume more dietary fiber**—in the form of fresh fruits, vegetables and whole grains. Fiber speeds the passage of feces through the intestines, reducing the amount of time any carcinogens present in the body remain in contact with body tissues.

•**Avoid processed foods.** Potato chips, baked goods and other processed foods tend to contain lots of trans fatty acids, refined sugar and/or sodium. Animal studies have linked each of these substances to cancer.

A SHIELD AGAINST CANCER

From the standpoint of cancer avoidance, virtually all fruits, vegetables and grains are beneficial. But certain plant foods are special—because they contain cancer-preventing compounds.

Eight plant foods are particularly rich sources of these *phytochemicals*. They should be eaten every day.

•**Onions and garlic.** The same sulfur compounds that give these herbs their characteristic aromas protect cells against oxidative damage. That's the first step in the cancer process.

Onions and garlic also block the formation of *nitrosamines*. These potent carcinogens are formed in the stomach following the consumption of cured meats and other nitrate-containing foods.

•**Crucifers.** Broccoli, cauliflower, cabbage and Brussels sprouts are rich sources of potent anticancer compounds known as *glucosinolates*.

Crucifer consumption has been linked with a reduced risk for lung and colon cancer.

•**Nuts and seeds.** In addition to antioxidants, nuts and seeds contain *protease inhibitors*. These compounds help block the growth of blood vessels that tumors need to obtain nutrients from the bloodstream.

•**Whole grains.** Oats, wheat and other grains contain fiber that helps isolate cancer-causing compounds and remove them from the body.

Flaxseed, rye and millet are rich in *lignans*. These compounds act as weak estrogens, helping stymie the growth of breast cancer and other malignancies that are often estrogen-dependent.

•**Legumes.** Beans, peas and lentils are rich in fiber and *saponins*, compounds that block tumor growth by inhibiting DNA synthesis. Soybeans are the most potent anticancer legume.

•**Fruits.** In addition to vitamin C—a potent antioxidant—citrus fruits contain cancer-fighting compounds known as *monoterpenes* and *glutathiones*.

Ellagic acid—in blackberries, strawberries and raspberries—binds to carcinogens and thereby deactivates them.

•**Tomatoes.** Tomatoes get their red color from *lycopene*, a phytochemical that blocks the formation of carcinogens. Lycopene appears to be especially effective at preventing prostate cancer.

Important: Lycopene is more easily absorbed from cooked tomatoes than from raw tomatoes.

•**Umbellifers.** Carrots, parsley, celery and the spices cumin, anise, caraway and coriander are rich sources of phytochemicals.

The *carotenoids* in carrots are strong antioxidants. Compounds found in celery boost the action of the carcinogen-deactivating enzyme *glutathione S-transferase*.

Amazing Cancer Stoppers

Patrick Quillin, PhD, RD, clinical nutritionist in San Diego, CA, and former vice president of nutrition, Cancer Treatment Centers of America. *www.nutritioncancer.com.* He is author of numerous books, including *Beating Cancer with Nutrition.* Nutrition Times.

Every year, more than 1.4 million Americans are diagnosed with cancer. Nearly half of all Americans eventually will get the disease—and about 25% of them will die from it. But there is a powerful way to reduce your risk of getting cancer.

Specific nutrients and foods can help prevent or correct cellular, hormonal and other imbalances that may lead to cancer. The supplements mentioned here are available at health-food stores and some supermarkets.

FISH OIL

The most common nutritional deficiency in Americans is low *eicosapentaenoic acid* (EPA). It is one of the omega-3 fatty acids found in the oil of fatty fish, such as salmon and tuna. A healthy diet has a 1:1 ratio of omega-3 to omega-6 fatty acids (found in vegetable oils). The typical American diet has a 1:16 ratio.

EPA helps prevent cancer by improving cell membrane dynamics—the ability of each cell to receive hormones and signals from other cells while absorbing essential nutrients and expelling waste products. EPA also boosts immune function and lowers levels of hormones, such as *estradiol,* that contribute to breast and other cancers.

What I recommend to my patients: One tablespoon of fish oil daily. For capsules, follow dosage recommendations on labels. Carlson Laboratories, Dr. Sears, Nordic Naturals and Pharmax brands are reliable. Take it in the middle of a meal to avoid "fishy" belching or reflux.

CLA

Another fat that helps prevent cancer is *conjugated linoleic acid* (CLA), found in the meat and milk of grass-eating animals, such as cattle, sheep and goats. CLA helps build healthy cell membranes, allowing cells to absorb nutrients, process hormones and expel waste. It's hard to find CLA-rich foods in markets because most livestock in America are fed grain, not grass.

What I recommend to my patients: Three grams of CLA a day. You can get that from an eight-ounce serving of grass-fed beef. Look for such brands as Lasater Grasslands Beef, available at specialty food stores. On days when you don't eat grass-fed red meat, you can take a CLA supplement—three one-gram soft-gel capsules a day.

VITAMIN D

People living in Boston have, on average, double the risk of breast, colon and prostate cancers, compared with residents of San Diego.

Why? Many scientists think it's because Bostonians, like other northerners, don't get enough vitamin D, which is produced when skin is exposed to sun. Vitamin D is one of the most powerful anticancer nutrients. It facilitates the absorption of calcium, a mineral that not only builds strong bones but also is critical for "telegraphing" messages between cells. Poor cell-to-cell communication can contribute to cancer. Studies show that levels of vitamin D in fortified foods rarely equal the claims made on the labels. There is a debate as to whether synthetic vitamin D—the kind found in supplements—provides the same cancer protection as the naturally produced variety.

What I recommend to my patients: During the summer, get 15 minutes a day of midday sunshine with no sunscreen (without burning) on your face and bare arms. The body stockpiles vitamin D in the liver, so you're set for the rest of the year.

VITAMIN C

In a report published in *American Journal of Clinical Nutrition,* 33 of 46 studies showed that vitamin C protects against cancer. Cancer feeds on blood sugar (glucose)—and lowering chronically high blood sugar is crucial to preventing cancer. When you get enough vitamin C, you cut in half the amount of blood sugar that enters cells.

What I recommend to my patients: 500 to 1,000 milligrams (mg) of vitamin C a day, in three divided doses, taken with meals. Cancer patients may need higher doses, which usually are given intravenously.

Other ways to normalize blood sugar levels include regular exercise, weight loss and a diet that emphasizes lean meats, beans, nuts and produce. Five daily servings of fruits and vegetables nets you 300 mg of vitamin C.

SELENIUM

In the four-year Nutritional Prevention of Cancer Trial, scientists gave 1,312 participants either 200 micrograms (mcg) of the trace mineral selenium or a placebo. The results showed that selenium lowered the risk of prostate cancer by 63%, colon cancer by 58% and lung cancer by 46%.

Selenium strengthens the immune system, helps repair DNA damage and protects cells against toxins.

What I recommend to my patients: 200 mcg of selenium a day. Look for *selenomethionine*—selenium bound in yeast—which is absorbed the best. A particularly good food source is Brazil nuts (four nuts provide 200 mcg).

Caution: More is not better in this case. Selenium supplements in doses of 2,000 mcg or higher can be toxic.

GREEN TEA

Literally hundreds of studies have proven that green tea and its various extracts can prevent and, in some experiments, reverse cancer. These extracts work by different mechanisms, among them *apoptosis* ("programmed cell death"). In other words, green tea orders cancer cells to commit suicide.

What I recommend to my patients: Drink three eight-ounce cups of green tea a day. If you don't like the taste, take supplements of green tea extract, available in capsules, following the dosage recommendation on the label.

KILLER CONSTIPATION

Chronic constipation creates toxemia in the colon. Cancer-causing chemicals from the environment are ingested but not expelled quickly. Normally friendly food-digesting bacteria then produce toxins that end up in the bloodstream.

What I recommend to my patients: To ensure a daily bowel movement, get plenty of high-fiber foods…drink 64 ounces of filtered or bottled water a day…and exercise regularly. Prune juice and figs often relieve constipation. Or try a gentle herbal laxative, such as *psyllium* (Metamucil), following the dosage recommendation on the label.

Surprising Study About Breast Cancer

Taking an Advil or Motrin tablet might help save your life. Ibuprofen—the active ingredient in these over-the-counter pain medicines—may protect against breast cancer.

Recent study: Women who took two or more ibuprofen tablets every week for more than 10 years decreased breast cancer risk by 49%, compared with a 28% reduction for women who took aspirin.

Caution: Long-term use of ibuprofen or aspirin may cause stomach trouble—consult your doctor.

Randall E. Harris, MD, PhD, professor of preventive medicine and public health, The Ohio State University College of Medicine and Public Health, Columbus, and lead researcher, National Cancer Center's Women's Health Initiative Observational Study of 90,000 women, reported in *Proceedings*.

Mayo Clinic: New Scans Help Find Small Tumors

Mayo Clinic news release.

A new technique that uses a specially designed gamma camera was found to improve the detection of small breast tumors, according to a study.

TECHNIQUE ALLOWS EARLIER DETECTION

A team from the Mayo Clinic in Rochester, Minnesota, used the technique, called *molecular breast imaging*, on 40 women who had suspicious mammogram findings.

The imaging detected 33 of the 36 malignant lesions that were confirmed in 26 of the women during surgery.

Overall, molecular breast imaging had an 86% detection rate of small breast tumors.

"By optimizing the camera to detect smaller breast lesions, this technique should aid in the detection of early-stage breast cancer, something that was not possible with conventional gamma cameras," says Dr. Michael O'Connor, a Mayo Clinic radiologist.

BETTER THAN MAMMOGRAPHY

Mammography uses differences in the anatomic appearance of tumors and normal tissue to detect breast cancer. These differences can be subtle and can often be obscured by dense breast tissue.

In contrast, molecular breast imaging detects cancer by identifying differences in the metabolic behavior of tumors and normal tissue.

"Approximately 25% to 40% of women have dense breast tissue, which decreases the chance that a cancer will be visible on their mammograms," says Dr. Douglas Collins, another Mayo radiologist.

"With molecular breast imaging, the visibility of the tumor is not influenced by the density of the surrounding tissue, so this technique is well-suited to find cancers in women whose mammograms may not be very accurate," Collins explains.

Avoid Skin Cancer... Debunk the Myths

Barney Kenet, MD, dermatologist specializing in skin cancer. He is an assistant attending physician at New York-Presbyterian Hospital–Weill Medical College of Cornell University, and is coauthor (with Patricia Lawler) of *Saving Your Skin—Prevention, Early Detection, and Treatment of Melanoma and Other Skin Cancers*. Four Walls Eight Windows.

Everyone knows that excessive sun exposure is dangerous, yet up to 50% of people over age 65 are diagnosed with melanoma or some other type of skin cancer.

Why? Even health-savvy individuals remain confused about the best ways to adequately protect their skin.

Here are three of the most dangerous myths...

Myth #1: A beach umbrella keeps you safe from the sun.

Reality: When you're at the beach, a large percentage of ultraviolet (UV) light bounces off the sand onto your skin, even if you're under an umbrella. Water and snow have the same reflective effect.

When boating or sitting beneath a beach umbrella, apply sunscreen to all exposed areas, including your face and neck—even if you're wearing a brimmed hat. When skiing, apply sunscreen to your face and neck.

Myth #2: Sunscreen with a sun-protection factor (SPF) of 45 is three times more effective than SPF 15.

Reality: Most doctors recommend using a sunscreen with an SPF of at least 15. A higher SPF will not give you much additional protection. A sunscreen with an SPF of 45 is only about 5% more protective than an SPF 15 sunscreen. The higher-rated sunscreen doesn't last any longer, either.

All sunscreens need to be reapplied every two hours—and whenever you're exposed to water. This includes "waterproof" sunscreens, which provide some protection while swimming but still must be reapplied.

Make sure your sunscreen is labeled "broad spectrum"—meaning it blocks both ultraviolet A (UVA) and ultraviolet B (UVB) rays. Look for titanium dioxide or Parsol 1789 in the list of ingredients on the label.

Myth #3: Sunscreen provides complete sun protection.

Reality: While sunscreen is essential, there are other steps you also should take. The most important is to minimize sun exposure between 10 am and 4 pm, when the sun's rays are most intense. Hit the beach in the early morning or late afternoon instead.

To protect commonly neglected areas, wear...

●**UV-protective lip balm** with an SPF of 15 or higher.

●**A hat with a three-inch brim.** Baseball caps don't protect the ears or the back of the neck—common skin cancer sites, especially for golf and tennis players.

●**UV-protective sunglasses.** UV exposure can cause cataracts.

●**Sun-protective clothing.** UV rays can pass through many fabrics, including cotton. If you hold a garment up to a light and can see the shape of the bulb shining through, it's not providing adequate sun protection.

Many companies now offer lightweight, tightly woven garments designed for comfort and maximum protection.

Example: Solumbra 30+ SPF sun protective clothing, 800-882-7860, *www.sunprecautions.com.*

If you will be outdoors and don't have any special clothing, be sure to wear sunscreen *under* your shirt.

The Amazing Powers Of Aspirin

Charles H. Hennekens, MD, DrPH, professor of medicine, epidemiology and public health, University of Miami School of Medicine. He is a leading expert on low-dose aspirin for the treatment and prevention of cardiovascular disease and was the founding principal investigator for the Harvard-based Physicians' Health Study and Women's Health Study.

Aspirin is one of the best treatments for fever, headache and other aches and pains. It also is the safest and least expensive drug for preventing heart attacks—and it can greatly increase survival in those who have just had a heart attack.

Recent research suggests that aspirin may have other important uses as well. It prevents colon cancer and may prevent breast cancer. It may even slow the progression of Alzheimer's disease.

Important: Don't exceed the recommended dosage on the label *without consulting your doctor.* Regular use can cause intestinal upset or bleeding, although these side effects are rare at the low doses required for prevention of chronic diseases.

Here, a look at the latest findings…

HEART ATTACK PREVENTION

Most heart attacks occur when a clot in a coronary artery prevents blood from reaching the heart. Aspirin blocks the effects of *thromboxane A2,* a substance that initiates clotting. The Physicians' Health Study (PHS), a landmark study that followed 22,071 men age 40 and older, showed that aspirin reduced the risk of a first heart attack by 44%.

New finding: It is now believed that inflammation in the arteries may be just as important as blood clots in causing heart attacks. In the PHS, patients with the highest levels of *C-reactive protein,* a marker of inflammation, had a 52% drop in heart attack risk when taking aspirin.

The aspirin dose currently recommended to reduce clotting is too low to have a significant effect on inflammation. Studies are under way to determine if higher doses of aspirin would be beneficial.

Who should consider aspirin: Anyone who has a history of heart problems or a greater-than-10% risk of having a heart attack within the next decade based on a standardized scoring method developed by the Framingham Heart Study. (Ask your doctor to calculate your risk, or go to *www.nhlbi.nih.gov/about/framingham/riskabs.htm.*) Those at risk include many men over age 40 and women who are over age 50—especially those who smoke or have high cholesterol or high blood pressure. There would be 100,000 fewer first heart attacks each year if patients in these groups took aspirin regularly.

Dose: Up to 325 milligrams (mg)—one adult aspirin—daily. A dose as low as 81 mg (one baby aspirin) daily can be effective.

New warning #1: If you have a history of heart problems, don't stop taking aspirin without talking to your cardiologist. Patients routinely are advised to stop taking aspirin before surgery or other invasive procedures, such as colonoscopy, tooth extraction and biopsy, to reduce the risk of bleeding.

Recent study: More than 4% of 1,236 heart patients who stopped taking aspirin had coronary "events," such as a heart attack, within one week.

New warning #2: Take aspirin at least two hours before other nonsteroidal anti-inflammatory drugs (NSAIDs). Data from the PHS found that men who regularly took aspirin and other NSAIDs, such as *ibuprofen* and *naproxen,* had no reduction in heart attack risk. That's because NSAIDs can inhibit aspirin's heart-protecting effects.

DURING A HEART ATTACK

In a study of more than 17,000 heart attack patients, those given aspirin during a heart attack had a 23% lower death rate during the first 35 days as well as significant decreases in subsequent heart attacks and strokes.

Taking aspirin inhibits the activity of blood platelets, responsible for clotting, within 10 to 15 minutes.

The clot-dissolving drug *streptokinase,* routinely given after heart attacks, decreases the death rate by 25% but causes hemorrhagic stroke (bleeding in the brain) in about three of every 1,000 patients. It also has to be given within six hours of a heart attack to be effective. Aspirin has a much longer "therapeutic window"—24 hours after the onset of heart attack symptoms.

Dose: 325 mg at the first sign of symptoms, such as chest pain or pressure, shortness of breath, light-headedness or pain that spreads to the shoulder, neck or arms. Be sure to tell emergency personnel that you have taken aspirin.

Important: If the tablet is coated, crush it before taking to hasten absorption. If the person having a heart attack is unconscious, put a noncoated 325-mg aspirin under his/her tongue.

MIGRAINE

Migraine sufferers have a 20% to 30% decrease in attacks when they take aspirin every other day. Platelets contain *histamine*, a chemical that triggers spasms in brain blood vessels, causing pain.

Aspirin makes platelets less "sticky" and inhibits the release of histamine.

New finding: Aspirin is as effective as *sumatriptan* (Imitrex), a prescription migraine drug. A study of migraine patients showed that those who took high doses of aspirin at the onset of symptoms had a better response and fewer side effects than those taking intravenous Imitrex.

Dose: 81- to 325-mg aspirin daily or every other day for prevention…at least 1,000 mg for an acute attack.

ARTHRITIS

Aspirin inhibits the synthesis of *prostaglandins*, chemicals that cause inflammation and pain. It's the best NSAID for any condition that involves inflammation, such as arthritis. If arthritis pain is managed with other medication, low-dose aspirin therapy also should be considered to reduce the risk of cardiovascular disease. Patients with rheumatoid arthritis have a higher risk of cardiovascular disease.

Dose: Two 325-mg tablets six times daily…or two 500-mg tablets four times a day for treatment and prevention.

COLON CANCER

Aspirin reduces the risk of colorectal cancer. Researchers looked at more than 1,100 people diagnosed with colon cancer. Those given aspirin had a lower incidence of recurring polyps, and their risk of advanced lesions declined by more than 40%.

Aspirin is thought to block two enzymes, *cyclooxygenase 1* and *cyclooxygenase 2*, inhibiting the growth of cancer cells and their ability to establish a blood supply.

Dose: 81-mg aspirin daily if you have a family history of colorectal cancer or other risk factors, such as polyps.

MORE RESEARCH NEEDED

●**Breast cancer.** Women who take aspirin seven or more times a week are 26% less likely to get the most common form of breast cancer. Between 60% and 70% of breast cancer cases are estrogen receptor–positive, meaning that the presence of estrogen causes tumors to grow. It's thought that aspirin blocks an enzyme used in estrogen production.

Even though women taking aspirin for other conditions may gain protection against breast cancer, the research is too preliminary to recommend aspirin solely for this purpose.

●**Alzheimer's disease.** Alzheimer's patients who take aspirin regularly perform better on language, memory and other cognitive tests. Aspirin reduces brain inflammation and improves circulation—but it's still not clear if it slows the progression of the disease.

●**Gum disease.** Studies suggest that aspirin may reduce the risk of periodontal disease, probably due to its anti-inflammatory and antiplatelet effects. If you have gum disease, ask your dentist if aspirin might be effective for you.

Prevent Diabetes With Vitamin D

With type 1 diabetes, white blood cells attack and destroy insulin-producing pancreatic cells. Vitamin D receptors, which attach to white blood cells, reduce the chance that this will happen. In addition, vitamin D appears to improve the ability of cells to accept insulin for better glucose uptake, helping to prevent type 2 diabetes.

Best: Get 10 to 15 minutes of sunlight daily without sunscreen. Get 400 to 600 international units (IU) of vitamin D daily (through diet and supplements).

Foods high in vitamin D: Salmon, eggs, sardines, herring and milk.

Mark A. Stengler, ND, naturopathic physician in private practice, La Jolla, CA, and associate clinical professor of family medicine, Bastyr University, Kenmore, WA. He is coauthor of *Prescription for Natural Cures* (John Wiley & Sons) and author of *The Natural Physician's Healing Therapies* (Bottom Line Books).

Secrets to Living Longer: Miraculous Antiaging Supplements

Ronald Klatz, MD, president, American Academy of Anti-Aging Medicine, Chicago, *www.worldhealth.net*, and cofounder and vice president, National Academy of Sports Medicine, Calabasas, CA. He is author of numerous books, including *The New Anti-Aging Revolution.* Basic Health.

Aging damages the cells in our bodies—in our eyes, ears, brain, heart, lungs, skin, etc. The cells are assaulted by free radicals (by-products of the cells' normal metabolism) as well as by sunlight and pollutants. The accumulation of toxins hinders cell growth and repair. If we can prevent or reverse this cell damage, we can slow aging and live longer.

An important way to fight cell damage is with antiaging supplements. Below are seven of the most effective. You can choose to take one, several or all of them.

Important: Don't take supplements without the approval of a qualified physician. To find one experienced in antiaging medicine, contact the American Academy of Anti-Aging Medicine at 773-528-4333 or go to the organization's Web site, *www.worldhealth.net*, and click on "Directory," then go to "Physicians."

ALPHA-GPC

Derived from soy, this nutrient provides high levels of *choline*, which protects brain cells. It also increases levels of the neurotransmitter *acetylcholine*, which triggers an increased release of human growth hormone (HGH)—a hormone that is naturally present in the human body when we're young but that decreases steadily as we age.

Studies show that increased HGH can reduce body fat, boost energy levels and restore youthful immune function.

In animal studies, alpha-GPC corrected age-related brain decline. In human studies, it helped stroke victims retain cognitive functioning and improved the mental functioning and mood of people with dementia.

Dose: 600 to 1,200 milligrams (mg) per day.*

*Dosages vary by body weight. Consult your doctor for more details.

ASHWAGANDHA ROOT

This herb is used extensively in Ayurveda, the traditional medicine of India. It stimulates immunity and, as an antioxidant, reduces cell-damaging free radicals, particularly within brain cells. Its anti-inflammatory properties have been shown to be helpful for such inflammatory conditions as arthritis.

In one study, it increased oxygen-carrying hemoglobin, which rejuvenates cells. In addition, 70% of the men in the study said that their sexual performance improved—some men have even reported fewer gray hairs.

Dose: 3 to 6 grams (g) of the dried root in capsule form per day.

BETA-GLUCAN

This nutrient is derived from baker's yeast, young rye plants and medicinal mushrooms. It activates *macrophages*, key immune cells that fight bacteria, viruses and other disease-causing organisms. Beta-glucan enhances the effectiveness of conventional antibiotic therapy. It acts as a free-radical scavenger, removing cells damaged by exposure to radiation, chemotherapy and pollutants. It also lowers total and LDL ("bad") cholesterol while increasing HDL ("good") cholesterol. In addition, it reduces the risk of infection by stimulating white blood cell activity.

Dose: 300 to 1,000 mg per day.

LEMON BALM

Lemon balm is an important antioxidant. It contains a high concentration of *phenols*, chemicals that fight cell-damaging toxins. This herb can improve sleep…decrease the pain of inflammatory conditions such as arthritis…boost mental functioning…and combat viruses and bacteria.

Dose: 1,000 to 1,500 mg per day.

Caution: Avoid lemon balm if you have glaucoma. Some animal studies have shown that it may raise pressure in the eye, which can worsen the condition.

OMEGA-3 FATTY ACIDS

Omega-3 fatty acids, also called essential fatty acids (EFAs), aren't manufactured by the human body and must be supplied by diet or supplements. They are found primarily in fish but also are present in smaller amounts in green, leafy vegetables…soybeans…nuts…and flaxseed and canola oils.

Omega-3s decrease blood levels of *triglycerides* (bad fats) and *homocysteine* (an artery-damaging amino acid) as well as lower blood pressure. They also help thin the blood, preventing blood clots. These effects lower the risk of heart disease and stroke, the number-one and number-three killers of Americans (cancer is number two).

Omega-3s also act as anti-inflammatories, helpful in the treatment of such autoimmune diseases as rheumatoid arthritis, chronic inflammatory bowel disease and psoriasis. They are a building block of the outer layer of brain cells and may help treat depression.

Dose: 3 to 10 g a day of fish oil capsules. Follow the instructions on the label.

Caution: If you have heart disease or diabetes, consult your doctor before taking these high doses, which may raise cholesterol and blood sugar levels.

To get omega-3 fatty acids in your diet, eat oily fish three to four times per week. These include mackerel, salmon, sea bass, trout, herring, sardines, sablefish (black cod), anchovies and tuna. Use omega-3–rich canola oil in cooking and salad dressings.

EVENING PRIMROSE OIL

Evening primrose oil is derived from the seeds of the evening primrose plant. The active ingredient is *gamma-linolenic acid* (GLA), an omega-6 fatty acid.

As the body ages, it loses its ability to convert the dietary fats into GLA. Supplementing with evening primrose oil is important in combating the general effects of aging. It also may help in treating rheumatoid arthritis, diabetes, nerve damage (neuropathy), multiple sclerosis and Alzheimer's-related memory problems.

Dose: 3,000 to 6,000 mg daily, which contains about 270 to 540 mg of GLA.

Caution: Evening primrose oil may worsen temporal-lobe epilepsy. It should be avoided by epileptics and schizophrenics who are prescribed phenothiazine epileptogenic drugs.

RESVERATROL

This is a naturally occurring antioxidant found in many plants—including the skins of grapes. Red wine is the main dietary source. Resveratrol decreases the "stickiness" of blood platelets, reducing the risk of blood clots. It also may help prevent the development and progression of various cancers.

Dose: 200 to 650 micrograms (mcg) daily. One eight-ounce glass of red wine contains roughly 640 mcg. Grapes, grape juice and raisins are *not* good sources.

Change Your Biological Age

William J. Evans, PhD, adviser to NASA and former head of its nutrition, physical fitness and rapid rehabilitation team. He is coauthor of *AstroFit: The Age-Reversal Program Used by Astronauts, Now Adapted for Everyone.* The Free Press.

Gray hair, wrinkled skin, flabbiness, loss of vitality and reduced resistance to injury and disease...

To most Americans, these are harbingers of old age, unwelcome but inevitable milestones along a path that leads inexorably to the grave. In fact, recent research suggests something quite different—that the body's gradual decline stems not from the passing of years but from the combined effects of inactivity and poor nutrition. So, no matter what your present health status or your chronological age, regular exercise and better eating habits can help lower your biological age.

Benefits: Reduced body fat...increased muscle mass...strength increases of 200% to 300%... increases in aerobic capacity of 20% or more... and reduced risk of heart disease, diabetes, osteoporosis and other age-related ailments.

Your goal should not be to become immortal, but to remain healthy and vigorous for as long as possible...and to compress the inevitable period of decline preceding death from several years into a few weeks or months.

To gauge your biological age: Forget how many birthdays you've marked...instead consider how you stack up in terms of the 10 key "biomarkers" identified by our lab...

●**Muscle mass.** As Americans move from adolescence to old age, we lose almost seven pounds of lean body mass each decade—a rate that accelerates after age 45.

Reduced muscle mass leads not only to reduced strength, but also to an increased risk of heart disease and diabetes, reduced aerobic capacity and a slower metabolism (which promotes fat gain). All of this happens because of bad habits like driving instead of walking or riding a bike, taking elevators rather than stairs…and because we're all too willing to let younger friends and relatives do chores we should do ourselves.

Good news: Those who remain physically active lose little muscle tissue as they age. All it takes is 20 to 30 minutes of aerobic exercise two or three times weekly.

•**Strength.** Between the ages of 20 and 70, the average American loses about 30% of his/ her muscle cells—including a large proportion of "fast-twitch" cells needed for sprinting and other high-exertion exercises.

Unchecked, this loss of muscle leads eventually to sarcopenia, the severe, debilitating weakness that makes independent living impossible.

Good news: While we cannot prevent the loss of muscle cells, a weight-lifting regimen will compensate by boosting the size and strength of the cells that remain.

Essential: Two or three sets of 10 lifts with a weight that should leave your muscles completely fatigued. If not, add more weight.

•**Metabolic rate.** Because more energy is needed to maintain muscle than fat, the less muscle tissue in your body, the slower your metabolism—and the fewer calories you must consume to maintain ideal body weight.

Beginning at age 20, the average person's metabolic rate drops about 2% per decade. Thus, the average 70-year-old needs 500 fewer calories a day than the average 25-year-old.

To fight fat, eat fewer calories and get enough exercise to maintain your muscle mass.

•**Body-fat percentage.** In most cases, advancing age brings not only muscle loss but fat gain. Even if our weight (as measured by a scale) changes little, the ratio of fat to lean tissue in our bodies can rise markedly over the years.

The body of the average 25-year-old woman is 25% fat, for example, while the average 65-year-old woman is about 43% fat.

For men, the numbers rise from 18% fat at age 25 to 38% at 65.

Danger: Excessive fat leads to chronic disease and premature death.

Especially dangerous: Fat around the waist. It's far more unhealthy than fat on the buttocks or thighs.

To lose fat and gain muscle: Combine some restriction in calories with regular exercise.

•**Aerobic capacity.** To gauge fitness, doctors often measure the body's ability to process oxygen during exercise. The greater this aerobic capacity, the faster oxygen is pumped throughout the body—and the fitter the individual.

Like other biomarkers, aerobic capacity often declines with age. Typically, by age 65 it is 30% to 40% below its level in young adulthood.

Good news: Regular aerobic exercise—the kind that causes huffing and puffing—will raise your aerobic capacity no matter what your present age.

•**Blood-sugar tolerance.** For most Americans, aging brings about a gradual decline in the body's ability to metabolize blood sugar (glucose). So common is this problem that by age 70, 20% of men and 30% of women are at an increased risk of diabetes, a potential killer.

At special risk for problems: People who are overweight, sedentary and those who eat a fatty diet.

Good news: A low-fat, high-fiber diet that restricts total calories consumed, combined with regular exercise, will cut your diabetes risk. Be sure to include both strength-building and aerobic exercise in your routine.

•**Cholesterol ratio.** As most of us know, high cholesterol boosts your risk of heart disease. But total cholesterol isn't the only thing that counts.

Very important: The ratio of total cholesterol to HDL (good) cholesterol. For older people, the ideal ratio is 4.5 or lower. A person whose total cholesterol is 200 and whose HDL is 50, for example, has a ratio of 200/50, or 4.0.

To lower your ratio: Stop smoking, lose weight, decrease your intake of fatty, cholesterol-rich foods (especially animal products) and exercise regularly, a good way to boost HDL levels.

•**Blood pressure.** In many parts of the world, advancing age brings little if any change in blood pressure.

In the US, however, where older people tend to be both overweight and sedentary, blood pressure does rise with age, often spiraling far above the maximum "safe" level.

To keep your pressure in check: Stay slim, don't smoke, get regular exercise and limit your consumption of fat, salt and alcohol. If these steps fail, pressure-lowering drugs may be necessary.

●**Bone density.** As we age, our skeletons slowly become weaker and more brittle.

While some mineral loss is inevitable, the severe and potentially deadly condition known as osteoporosis is not.

Prevention: Although consuming at least 1,000 milligrams (mg) of calcium a day will retard the loss of bone, that alone rarely does the trick.

Also needed: Weight-bearing exercise, such as walking, running or aerobics.

Not helpful for bones: Swimming and other forms of exercise that do not subject the long bones of the body to the stress of weight-bearing activity.

●**Temperature regulation.** Our ability to control our internal body temperature declines as we get older, due to a reduction in our ability both to shiver, which raises body temperature, and to sweat, which lowers it. This means cold and hot weather pose a danger to elderly people. To some extent, this can't be avoided.

Regular aerobic exercise causes you to sweat more readily whenever you exert yourself, not just during exercise. It also increases your total blood volume—which will make you less likely to overheat or dehydrate in hot weather.

Important: Force yourself to drink during exercise and in hot weather, even if you're not thirsty. In winter, be sure to dress warmly in layers.

How to Feel And Look Younger

David Ryback, PhD, an antiaging/stress reduction consultant in Atlanta. He is author of *Look 10 Years Younger, Live 10 Years Longer,* which is available in editions for men and for women. Galahad Books.

Following are five strategies that will really help you to feel and look younger than you actually are…

●**Practice stretching each morning.** Regular stretching helps you feel more flexible and, as a result, you will feel and look younger. By stretching, you relax your muscles, and movements become more graceful and youthful.

●**Stand up straight.** By maintaining good posture, you'll look 10 pounds thinner. Practice in front of the mirror, and you'll notice that your stomach looks flatter, your torso appears longer and thinner—and you don't have that old, tired, hunched look.

●**Exercise at least 15 minutes a day.** Physical activity alleviates depression and improves your mood. It also sends more blood to the skin, giving your complexion a healthy, rosy and youthful glow.

●**Eat more fruits and vegetables.** A vegetarian or even a semi-vegetarian diet that includes lots of fruits, vegetables and grains will help you maintain a stable energy level. By eating sensibly, you can increase your energy level and feel younger.

●**Reduce stress.** If left unchecked, stress puts unnecessary wear and tear on your body's internal organs, which causes you to look tired and years older.

Eyesight Danger

Sunlight's blue wavelengths can contribute to macular degeneration, the main cause of blindness in people older than 55.

Most susceptible: People with fair skin and light eyes.

Self-defense: Wear yellow or amber sunglasses (they also block UV rays).

For healthy eyes: Don't smoke, and avoid secondhand smoke…eat dark green, leafy vegetables and foods with omega-3 fatty acids, such as flaxseeds and fish.

Lylas G. Mogk, MD, founding director, Visual Rehabilitation and Research Center, Grosse Pointe, MI, and co-author of *Macular Degeneration: The Complete Guide to Saving and Maximizing Your Sight.* Ballantine.

Live Longer, Feel Better

Mark A. Stengler, ND, naturopathic physician in private practice, La Jolla, CA, and associate clinical professor of family medicine, Bastyr University, Kenmore, WA. He is coauthor of *Prescription for Natural Cures* (John Wiley & Sons) and author of *The Natural Physician's Healing Therapies* (Bottom Line Books).

We age when the body's cells die at faster rates than new ones are generated. Many of us age prematurely because the traditional American diet hastens cellular destruction and boosts the already too-high rate of obesity, diabetes, cancer and other chronic diseases.

The body produces enormous quantities of highly reactive oxygen molecules, called free radicals, when we eat high-fat foods…are exposed to environmental pollutants, such as pesticides and ultraviolet radiation…or consume too many calories. Free radicals attack healthy cells and accelerate the aging process.

I advise my patients to take a high-potency multivitamin/mineral supplement. This offers general protection against free radicals and helps eliminate toxins.

Caution: Don't choose a formula that contains iron unless you have been diagnosed with iron-deficiency anemia. High levels of iron can be toxic.

In addition, I suggest the following…

TAKE SPIRULINA

Spirulina is a blue-green algae that grows wild in warm waters around the world. It has become a staple in Africa because it contains all the essential amino acids in a highly absorbable form and is a rich source of protein. It also contains *carotenoids*, fat-soluble pigments that act as antioxidants…*gamma-linoleic acid* (GLA), an essential fatty acid…*chlorophyll*, a pigment that has potent antioxidant and anticancer properties…and *phytocyanins*, which stimulate red blood cell production.

Several studies have shown that spirulina improves immune system activity. In one study, tobacco chewers who had mouth cancer were given one gram of spirulina daily for a year. Nearly half of those who took the supplement showed improvement, while only three of 43 in the nonsupplement group had any reversal of symptoms. Spirulina also has been shown

to have antiviral effects and a mild cholesterol-reducing benefit.

What I recommend to my patients: Take 2,000 to 3,000 milligrams (mg) per day.

EAT BERRIES

Strawberries, raspberries and blueberries—as well as grapes and cherries—all contain phytonutrients known as *flavonoids*, which have potent antioxidant activity that can fight heart disease. The fruits' ellagic acid promotes excretion of carcinogenic chemicals.

Trap: Soft fruits, such as berries and grapes, absorb pesticides more readily than firm produce, such as apples and oranges. Be sure to eat organic.

What I recommend to my patients: Eat one-half cup of berries, cherries or grapes or drink four ounces of purple grape juice or red wine daily.

DRINK GREEN TEA

Green tea comes from the leaves of *Camellia sinensis*, the same plant used to make black tea—but because it's processed differently, it has more of the potent antioxidants called polyphenols than black tea. The most potent is *epigallocatechin gallate* (EGCG).

Green tea helps protect the liver and fight cancer. One study looked at 472 Japanese women with breast cancer. Increased green tea consumption was associated with a decreased risk of lymph node metastasis. Researchers also found that when women with breast cancer drank five cups of green tea a day, they were more likely to be in remission six months later.

Green tea also has been shown to reduce cholesterol levels, fight tooth decay and aid in weight loss.

What I recommend to my patients: Drink two or more cups of green tea daily. If you don't like tea, you can take 1,500 mg daily of a green tea extract formula that contains 35% to 55% EGCG.

LIMIT DAIRY

Milk, cheese and other dairy foods contain *casein*, one of the most common food allergens. It can deplete immune cells.

Milk also contains *xanthine oxidase*, an enzyme that may increase the buildup of plaque in the arteries.

You don't need dairy to get enough calcium. Substitute with calcium-enriched foods, such as juice and soy, rice and almond milk. Broccoli, collard greens, sardines and canned salmon with bones also are rich in calcium.

What I recommend to my patients: No more than five servings of dairy a week.

SELECT EZEKIEL BREAD

Ezekiel bread, a type of bread found in health-food stores, uses younger sprouted grains, which have a higher nutritional content than typical mature grains. If you can't find Ezekiel bread, choose other breads with whole grains (wheat, amaranth, spelt, etc.).

All whole grains are rich in fiber, which prevents constipation and reduces toxins in the digestive tract. They also contain phytonutrients, which block free-radical damage and improve immune function.

What I recommend to my patients: Eat at least one slice of Ezekiel bread a day.

TAKE FISH OIL AND EVENING PRIMROSE OIL

Both of these oils contain essential fatty acids—fish oil is a source of *eicosapentanoic acid* (EPA) and *docosahexanoic acid* (DHA)...evening primrose oil is a source of GLA.

Fatty acids are involved in proper functioning of the brain and immune system. They also reduce the risk of heart disease and cancer...and relieve pain.

What I recommend to my patients: Take 3,000 to 5,000 mg of fish oil and 1,000 mg of evening primrose oil daily. If you are on blood-thinning medications such as *warfarin* (Coumadin), check with your doctor first. Strict vegetarians can substitute flaxseed oil or hemp oil for fish oil (one to two tablespoons daily).

EAT GARLIC

Garlic contains *allicin*, a sulfur compound that builds immunity and prevents infections. It reduces the risk of colon, esophageal and stomach cancers. One study of 41,000 American women found that one or more servings of garlic a week decreased colon cancer risk by 35%. It also lowers cholesterol and has mild blood pressure–lowering effects.

What I recommend to my patients: One-half to one whole raw clove daily (cooking reduces its benefits)—or an odor-free supplement containing 4,000 to 5,000 micrograms (mcg) of allicin.

DINE EARLY

Americans typically have their dinner a few hours before bedtime—but studies have shown that digestive juices lose potency later in the day. This means that you absorb fewer nutrients and have more trouble metabolizing toxins.

What I recommend to my patients: Eat no later than 7 pm.

Managing Menopause Without Drugs... Commonly Overlooked Strategies that Really Work

Toni M. Cutson, MD, associate professor of community and family medicine and associate professor of medicine, Duke University Medical Center, Durham, NC. She is co-author of "Managing Menopause," a report published in *American Family Physician*.

Hot flashes, mood swings, vaginal dryness, sleep disturbances and osteoporosis are some of the symptoms that affect about 75% of menopausal women.

To help control these common problems, doctors in the past often prescribed hormone replacement therapy (HRT). However, HRT has been linked to an increased risk for breast cancer, stroke and blood clots. Therefore, many women have decided to treat their symptoms with a wide variety of nondrug alternatives—eating a low-fat, high-fiber diet...exercising on a regular basis...and quitting smoking.

These are a good start. But there are additional ways to relieve the symptoms. *A woman can benefit from these eight commonly overlooked strategies...*

•**Eat at least eight servings of fruits and vegetables each day.** These high-fiber, low-fat foods are typically rich in folic acid and other B vitamins, which reduce the risk for heart disease by helping to prevent arterial blood clots.

One serving equals one piece of fruit, one-half cup of cooked vegetables or one cup of raw vegetables. It is actually surprisingly easy to get into the habit of eating many small, healthful snacks each day, and the benefits that it affords you are enormous.

Also, make sure to consume calcium-rich products, such as dairy products (milk and yogurt) and fortified orange juice to combat osteoporosis.

•**Eat whole soy foods.** They contain *isoflavones*, estrogen-like compounds that reduce hot flashes, bone loss and LDL ("bad") cholesterol. Sources include soy nuts, soy milk and tofu, and can usually be found in your local supermarket.

Caution: Avoid nutritional supplements and powders that claim to have the same active ingredients as soy foods. These products may contain unknown chemicals that could be harmful.

Worse, they may contain *excessive* levels of isoflavones, which increase breast cancer risk. Limit your soy intake to about 60 grams of isoflavones a day.

•**Take a daily multivitamin.** Choose a name brand, such as One-a-Day or Centrum, to get the recommended requirements for most vitamins and minerals. Do *not* take individual vitamin megadoses, however. They can be harmful.

Too much vitamin A, for example, can damage the eyes and skin. Megadoses of vitamin D can cause excess calcium in the bloodstream.

To prevent liver damage, avoid pills that provide more than 18 milligrams (mg) of iron. Because menopausal women no longer lose iron through menstruation, iron supplements make sense only if you've been diagnosed with an iron deficiency.

•**Take a calcium supplement.** A daily 1,500-mg dose helps prevent osteoporosis.

Calcium carbonate found in Tums is cheap and readily absorbed. Each Tums tablet provides 200 mg of calcium. For higher doses, try Tums E-X with 300 mg or Tums 500 with 500 mg.

•**Try proven herbal remedies.** Some menopausal women are now taking chasteberry in order to prevent hot flashes. But little scientific research exists to support its effectiveness.

Similarly, avoid dong quai and licorice root. Dong quai can cause excessive blood thinning. Licorice root may precipitate headaches or high blood pressure.

Better: Black cohosh. This herb suppresses *luteinizing hormone* (LH), which triggers hot flashes. Some women claim it also improves their sex drive and eases night sweats and sleep disturbances.

Black cohosh is sold as Remifemin at health-food stores.

•**Limit alcohol consumption.** Have no more than three glasses of wine—or three ounces of hard liquor—a week. Drinking wine in moderation may be beneficial to the heart, but too much alcohol exacerbates hot flashes.

•**Relax.** Many menopausal women blame hormone fluctuations for mood and memory problems. But psychological stress is often the real cause. While they're going through menopause, they may also be caring for elderly parents, sending children off to college or dealing with job stress.

To combat stress: Seek help if you find yourself in difficult situations…turn down extra projects at work…ask siblings to help care for an elderly parent…or find a day program that caters to the social needs of seniors.

Get plenty of restorative sleep and give yourself 30 minutes of quiet time each day. If your schedule is too hectic and doesn't permit this amount of time, five minutes is better than nothing.

•**Rethink your sex life.** The physical and psychological aspects of menopause often put a damper on a woman's sex life. But abstinence is not the answer.

Frequent sexual activity decreases vaginal dryness, improves sleep, reduces stress and helps alleviate moodiness.

Bonus: Regular sex also increases your libido.

Jump-Start Your Sex Life…Naturally

Chris D. Meletis, ND, dean of clinical affairs and chief medical officer, National College of Naturopathic Medicine, Portland, OR. He is author of *Better Sex Naturally.* HarperResource.

Well before *sildenafil* (Viagra), *vardenafil* (Levitra) and *tadalafil* (Cialis) people relied on aphrodisiacs to increase sexual desire…boost stamina…improve performance…and increase pleasure.

Many of these compounds owe their reputation to folklore, but several herbs and dietary supplements have proven sex-enhancing effects.

Good news: Products that improve sex naturally may be less likely to cause serious side effects than prescription drugs. Many strengthen the cardiovascular system and help regulate hormone production. That's as important for good sex as having an erection or being sufficiently lubricated.

Sex-enhancing herbs and supplements aren't taken just an hour or so before sex. They're taken daily until there's a noticeable improvement in sexual performance.

At that point, some people take a pause to see if the herbs and supplements are no longer necessary. Others continue taking the preparations indefinitely.

Important: Use herbs and supplements only under medical supervision to be sure to get the product and dosage that's right for you.

Caution: Fresh or dried herbs differ greatly in potency from batch to batch. Use capsules or tinctures, ideally ones that have been standardized to contain the proper amounts of active ingredients.

For better sex, try one of the following natural enhancers. Select the one that best suits your needs. Give each preparation a few months to work. If you see no effect, try another.

GINKGO BILOBA

Ginkgo contains a variety of compounds that relax blood vessels and increase circulation to the brain and pelvic area.

For women, increased blood flow improves vaginal lubrication and sexual responsiveness.

For men, adequate blood flow is essential to achieve and sustain erections.

Typical dosage: Capsules—40 to 60 milligrams (mg) of 24% standardized powdered extract three to four times daily. Tincture—30 drops three to four times daily.

Side effects: Ginkgo may cause dizziness, headache or heart palpitations.

Caution: Ginkgo is a blood thinner and can increase the blood-thinning effects of aspirin and *warfarin* (Coumadin). Check with your physician before using ginkgo if you're taking either medication.

MUIRA PUAMA

Also known as "potency wood," this herb contains sterols and other compounds that boost levels of testosterone, a hormone that plays a critical role in sexual desire in women and men.

Muira puama also contains volatile oils that are thought to restore sex drive by stimulating the brain's pleasure center.

Typical dosage: 250 mg three times daily in capsule form.

Side effect: Muira puama may lower blood pressure by as much as 10%. Check with your doctor before using this herb if you have low blood pressure (hypotension).

GINSENG

This herb is an "adaptogen," meaning it helps the body compensate for extended periods of stress. Stress can cause sexual desire and performance to plummet.

Compounds in ginseng root lower levels of adrenaline and other stress hormones.

These compounds also improve blood flow to the penis, help tissues use oxygen more efficiently and boost the production of testosterone in men and progesterone in women.

Typical dosage: Capsules—10 to 50 mg one to three times daily. Tincture—30 to 60 drops daily.

Side effect: Ginseng may cause diarrhea… high blood pressure…sleeplessness.

ASHWAGANDA

A member of the pepper family, this herb contains *withanolides*, substances that increase the activity of testosterone and progesterone.

Ashwaganda also relieves stress and anxiety.

Typical dosage: Capsules—1,000 mg once or twice daily. Tincture—60 to 90 drops two or three times daily.

Side effects: Because ashwaganda has anti-anxiety properties, it should not be used by anyone taking medications to treat anxiety and/or depression. The herb could intensify the drugs' actions as well as their side effects. Ashwaganda may also trigger miscarriages.

ARGININE

Taken in supplement form, this amino acid has been shown to relax smooth muscle contractions. This boosts arterial dilation, bringing more blood to the pelvic area.

The body uses arginine to produce nitric oxide, a chemical needed to achieve erections.

(Sildenafil works, in part, by making nitric oxide more readily available in the body.)

Typical dosage: 1,000 to 2,000 mg twice daily in capsule form. Take capsules between meals, since many foods contain lysine, an amino acid that counteracts arginine's effects.

Side effect: Don't take this herb if you get cold sores caused by the herpes simplex virus. Arginine stimulates viral replication.

FOR WOMEN ONLY

The herb *dong quai* contains plant sterols that help correct estrogen deficiencies.

Studies suggest that dong quai can increase sexual desire as well as the intensity of orgasms.

Typical dosage: Capsules—1,000 mg three to four times daily. Tincture—45 to 60 drops two or three times daily.

Caution: Pregnant and lactating women should not use dong quai. The herb can cause excessive blood thinning and also may increase sensitivity to sunlight.

Secrets of Much More Satisfying Sexuality— How to Have Great Sex Every Time

Edward W. Eichel, MA, a psychotherapist in private practice in New York City. He is the originator of the coital alignment technique (CAT), which is described in greater detail—and, yes, illustrated—in his book *The Perfect Fit.* Signet.

Of all the concerns voiced by women undergoing sex therapy, none is more common—or emotionally distressing—than an inability to achieve orgasm during intercourse.

Only about 30% of women achieve orgasm regularly during intercourse (coitus).

Some women endure years of sex without a single coital orgasm. Typically, a woman relies upon a partner who "jumps through hoops" to bring her there, but never achieves the ideal.

Result: Sexuality is robbed of its playfulness and spontaneity and becomes more a chore than a pleasure.

TO THE RESCUE

A variant of the standard missionary position—known as the *coital alignment technique* (CAT)—not only helps the woman achieve orgasm during coitus, but boosts the odds that she and her partner will climax simultaneously.

Men who have long considered themselves sexually inadequate, as well as women who have worried they were frigid, can begin to experience sex with all its physical pleasure and emotional intimacy.

Bonus: Because good sex is usually synonymous with good communication, this improvement in a couple's sex life often carries over into other aspects of their relationship, bringing new levels of intimacy, contentment and commitment—important in this age of AIDS and other sexually transmitted diseases.

Unlike some other alternative lovemaking techniques, CAT is relatively straightforward. Couples have differed in the time necessary to master the technique, but with persistence, most have succeeded. Once mastered, it is remarkably effective—and quite reliable.

Recent study: Sexual response was measured in couples involved in committed relationships—before and after receiving CAT training.

Prior to the CAT training, only 23% of the women reported achieving orgasm during intercourse on a regular basis. After CAT, that figure jumped to 77%.

Before CAT, no women reported having regular simultaneous orgasms with their partners. Afterward, one-third of the women reported doing so.

Almost all participants reported at least some improvement in their sex lives following CAT training. In fact, the only participants who failed to benefit were those whose relationships were already jeopardized by nonsexual issues.

CAT BASICS

CAT encompasses five distinct elements, each designed to maximize contact between the penis and the clitoris, thus maximizing sexual response in both partners...

•**Positioning.** The woman lies on her back. The man lies atop her, facing her much as in the conventional missionary position, but with his pelvis overriding hers in a "riding high" orientation. His penis should be inserted into her vagina, with its shaft pressed firmly against her *mons veneris*—the soft fleshy mound covering the pubic bone above the vagina. She wraps her legs around his thighs, with her legs bent at an angle not exceeding 45 degrees and her ankles resting on his calves.

Important: He must let his full weight fall on her and must avoid using his hands or elbows to support his weight. While she may find this uncomfortable initially, it is essential to keep his pelvis from sliding back down off of hers.

•**Limited movement.** Conventional intercourse involves a great deal of pushing, pulling and bracing of the arms and legs.

CAT coitus focuses on the couples pelvic movement. In fact, little additional movement is possible during CAT, given the partners' positioning. If additional movement is possible, the positioning is faulty.

•**Pressure-counterpressure.** During ordinary intercourse, the man sets the rhythm while the woman moves little, if at all. In contrast, CAT calls for a rhythmic movement that is virtually identical for both partners.

Procedure: She performs an upward stroke, forcing his pelvis backward. He allows his pelvis to move, yet maintains a continuous counterpressure against her pelvis (and her clitoris).

In the downward movement, the pattern of movement is then reversed, with the man pushing downward and the woman maintaining the counterpressure against his penis. As her pelvis moves backward and downward, the penis shaft rocks forward against her mons veneris, sliding to a shallow position in the vagina.

Note: Although the force of pressure and counterpressure is quite intense during CAT, the partners' actual movement is surprisingly slight.

•**Full genital contact.** Repeated thrusting of the penis into and out of the vaginal "barrel," typical of conventional missionary intercourse, affords little direct stimulation of the primary erogenous zones that facilitate a complete coital orgasm—the front base of the penis for the male

and the clitoris and the urethral meatus (tissue around the urinary opening) of the female.

Typical result: His orgasm, even if perceived as pleasurable, is far less powerful than it might be…and she, having gotten little if any clitoral stimulation, fails to climax at all.

In CAT, the penis and clitoris are held tightly together by pressure and counterpressure…and the penile-clitoral "connection" is rocked up and down in an evenly paced, lever-like fashion. This vibratory motion all but guarantees orgasms for both partners.

Bonus: Orgasms produced by CAT differ significantly from those produced by conventional in-and-out sex. Whereas a conventional orgasm is limited to a pulsating sensation, a CAT orgasm will combine this with a "melting" sensation.

Among 86 participants of the recent study, 90% of all subjects said that CAT intensified their orgasms…and 60% said that it increased their desire for more frequent sex.

•**"Passive" orgasm.** In ordinary coitus, the man thrusts faster and more deeply as he becomes increasingly aroused, while the woman typically slows down or even stops moving altogether. At the moment of climax, the partners' movements often become disconnected and may fall completely out of sync.

Result: The orgasm is incomplete.

Better: CAT prescribes complete coordination of movement by the partners, up to and beyond the moment of climax. In other words, both partners make no effort to "grab" for orgasm. Instead they let it "overtake" them. The transition from voluntary motion preceding orgasm to the reflexive, involuntary movements typical of orgasm itself is thus fully coordinated. The possibility of incomplete orgasm is drastically limited.

Crucial: A conscious effort by both partners not to hold their breath or suppress natural sounds. Breathing freely and giving full rein to sighs, grunts, moans, spoken words and other vocalizations greatly facilitate orgasm—for the noisemaker and the listener alike.

Some couples report that the "reversed" CAT (woman on top) is an effective variation of CAT—if the man is much heavier than his partner.

Supercharge Your Immunity with Just a Few Herbs

James A. Duke, PhD, leading authority on medicinal plants and former chief of the US Department of Agriculture Plant Laboratory. He is a distinguished lecturer at the Tai Sophia Institute, a center for patient care and graduate education in complementary medicine, Laurel, MD. He is author of *Dr. Duke's Essential Herbs*. St. Martin's Press.

Medicinal herbs are rich in antioxidants that maintain health and slow the aging process. They also can prevent or alleviate age-related problems, such as arthritis, high blood pressure and failing vision.

World-renowned botanist James A. Duke, PhD, feels that certain herbs are essential to healthy aging. Dr. Duke has a half-acre medicinal herb garden on his six-acre homestead in Fulton, Maryland. There are seven potent herbs that he uses himself.

While these herbs have no significant side effects and are far safer than most synthetic drugs, it is always wise to consult your doctor before treating a medical problem yourself.

Some herbs can interact with prescription and nonprescription drugs, magnifying or weakening their effects. In addition, some people may be allergic to herbs. Be alert to symptoms, such as a rash, when taking any herb.

With your doctor's approval, you can take these herbs all at the same time, along with vitamins, if you wish. Follow the dosages suggested on the labels.

BILBERRY: VISION DISORDERS

Bilberry is rich in *anthocyanins*, chemicals that keep the capillary walls strong and flexible. It also is loaded with antioxidants that defend delicate tissue against free-radical damage.

In particular, bilberry protects the retina and its blood supply, preventing and improving vision disorders, such as macular degeneration. Bilberry can ward off other eye problems, too, including cataracts, glaucoma and poor night vision.

ECHINACEA: COLDS AND FLU

Contrary to some recent reports, I believe that this herbal medicine is a powerful ally against colds and flu. The purple coneflower from which it comes has been used medicinally by Native Americans for centuries. At least three of the chemicals it contains—*caffeic acid, echinacoside* and *cichoric acid*—have known antiviral properties. Echinacea also boosts the body's own infection-fighting powers.

Take echinacea at the first sign of an upper-respiratory infection or flu. I also take it when I know I'll be in crowds or around other sources of infection.

This is not an herb for everyday use—the immune system may eventually stop responding to it. I don't take it for more than eight weeks in a row.

GARLIC: BLOOD PRESSURE AND CHOLESTEROL

This pungent bulb was prescribed by Hippocrates, the fifth-century BC Greek physician, and cited as a cure-all in an ancient Sanskrit manuscript. Today, we attribute its medicinal powers to a high concentration of sulfur compounds.

Garlic lowers blood pressure and cholesterol. In addition, there is evidence that garlic can reduce the risk of cancer, particularly in the gastrointestinal tract.

Garlic contains at least 25 germ-killing compounds working to fight bacterial, viral and fungal infections.

Eat at least one raw clove or four cooked cloves daily…or take garlic capsules.

HAWTHORN: POTENT HEART DRUG

An extract made from this flowering shrub can be useful against irregular heart rhythm, angina and shortness of breath. Hawthorn contains seven compounds known to prevent dangerous clotting and three that lower blood pressure. One study at the University of Madras in India suggests that hawthorn also may reduce cholesterol.

MILK THISTLE: LIVER PROTECTION

The liver, the organ vital to detoxifying the blood, is under constant assault by pollution. Alcohol, also, is bad for the liver. Milk thistle, a relative of the artichoke, appears to protect the liver. It contains *silymarin*, which strengthens cell membranes and boosts the organ's ability to repair itself. Milk thistle has even been used to treat hepatitis A and C.

I take milk thistle capsules when I'm traveling and will be exposed to smog. If I lived in a major city with pollution problems, I would take it every day.

I also take it before a celebration, when I may be drinking a bit more alcohol than usual.

You can take silymarin capsules or eat milk thistle seeds, available in health food stores, as you would sunflower seeds.

SAW PALMETTO: PROSTATE PROBLEMS

At least half of men over age 50 have difficulty urinating because benign prostate enlargement chokes off the flow. An extract of saw palmetto, a tropical shrub, has been used for years to treat this problem. A review in *The Journal of the American Medical Association* (JAMA) concluded that saw palmetto facilitates urination in men with prostate problems about as well as medication. Natural chemicals in the herb appear to block a testosterone-type hormone that promotes prostate growth. Men without prostate problems may choose to take it as a preventive measure.

Saw palmetto also may slow down male pattern baldness.

TURMERIC: HEART AND ARTHRITIS

This spice, made from the root of the tropical plant *Curcuma longa*, is a common ingredient in mustard and Indian food, and is what makes curry bright yellow. Turmeric is packed with antioxidants and contains powerful anti-inflammatory compounds called Cox-2 inhibitors.

Some research suggests turmeric can stop inflammation about half as effectively as steroids such as cortisone—but without the troubling side effects. This makes it a valuable ally against arthritis. In addition, turmeric protects the heart. It makes blood platelets less likely to clump and form dangerous clots. It also fights cholesterol buildup in the arteries.

Turmeric is available as an herbal preparation. You can also add turmeric to your diet when cooking. I like to use it to make a curried celery soup.

WHICH BRANDS TO BUY

Herbal products are sold by many manufacturers, but there is no federal regulation to ensure quality control.

To be safe, select major brands, such as Nature's Herb, Nature's Way and Solgar. These are available at most supermarkets, drugstores and health food stores. Buy preparations that clearly indicate on the labels the exact amounts of active ingredients.

Natural Ways to Lower Your Cholesterol

Marjory Abrams, publisher, *Bottom Line/Personal*, 281 Tresser Blvd., Stamford, CT 06901.

Tedd Mitchell, MD, medical director of the Cooper Wellness Program in Dallas (*www. cooperaerobics.com*) explains the most recent cholesterol guidelines, saying, "Many news reports have suggested that the new LDL ['bad' cholesterol] goal is 70 milligrams per deciliter (mg/dL) or less. In reality, this aggressively low target is only for people with a very high risk of heart attack—individuals with cardiovascular disease plus multiple risk factors [diabetes, continued smoking, high triglycerides and/or low HDL ('good') cholesterol].

"Goals for others range from 100 mg/dL or less (moderately high risk) to 160 or less (minimal risk). Consult your physician to determine your personal risk."

Cholesterol is an essential component of cell membranes. It also is required for the synthesis of estrogen, testosterone, adrenaline and other hormones. Even "bad" cholesterol is necessary for optimal health.

Dr. Mitchell says that many people can decrease LDL without taking statins by stepping up exercise and making dietary changes—reducing their intake of red meat and eggs...avoiding products that contain coconut oil and palm oil...increasing their intake of cholesterol-lowering margarine (Benecol, Smart Balance, etc.), oat bran and raw garlic. However, few people can cut LDL to 70 or less without taking Lipitor or another statin drug.

Integrative medicine expert Robban Sica, MD, medical director at the Center for Healing Arts, in Orange, Connecticut, suggests the following LDL-lowering supplements. *Dr. Sica starts most patients with one supplement and adds the others one by one in the order listed until the desired LDL level is met...*

•**Tocotrienols,** a form of vitamin E. Take 200 mg at dinner. Any other vitamin E supplement should be taken in the morning so that it doesn't interfere with tocotrienols.

•**Policosanol/guggulipid,** a sugarcane extract/herb combination. Take 500 mg with breakfast and dinner.

Caution: Policosanol and tocotrienols have a blood-thinning effect. Don't use them if you regularly use aspirin or other nonsteroidal anti-inflammatories (NSAIDs) or if you take *warfarin* (Coumadin).

•**Inositol hexaniacinate,** a timed-release niacin that, unlike other niacin supplements, does not cause flushing and is not toxic to the liver. Take 600 mg three times daily with meals.

•**Red yeast rice.** Take 800 mg twice daily. (This supplement is not safe for people who take statins.)

Her favorite suppliers: Thorne Research (800-228-1966, *www.thorne.com*) and Designs for Health (800-847-8302, *www.designsforhealth.com*).

Of course, always talk to your doctor before taking a new supplement or changing regimens on prescriptions.

Natural Remedies for Headache Pain

Alexander Mauskop, MD, associate professor of clinical neurology, State University of New York in Brooklyn and director, New York Headache Center, New York City. He is coauthor of *The Headache Alternative: A Neurologist's Guide to Drug-Free Relief.* Dell.

Which medication works best for headache pain? *That depends on the type of headache...*

•**Migraines** are usually treated with *sumatriptan* (Imitrex), *zolmitriptan* (Zomig) or another "triptan" drug.

•**Tension headaches** are usually treated with anti-inflammatory drugs like *ibuprofen* (Motrin) or *naproxen* (Aleve).

•**Cluster headaches** are usually treated with sumatriptan or inhaled oxygen.

These treatments are reliable and safe for occasional use. But when patients start to use headache medication more than twice a week, stomach upset and other side effects become a serious concern.*

*See a doctor at once if your headache is accompanied by confusion, convulsions or loss of consciousness...pain in the eye or ear...slurred speech, numbness, blurred vision or trouble walking...fever or nausea.

For this reason, headache sufferers should be sure to ask their doctors about trying nondrug approaches as well.

DIETARY MODIFICATION

Chronic headaches often have their origins in food sensitivities. *To identify the food or foods underlying your pain, try this elimination diet...*

•**For one week,** keep a list of all foods and beverages you consume. Be sure you also include seasonings.

•**For the next 30 days,** avoid all of the foods and beverages you consumed during the 24 hours preceding each headache you had during the week.

•**After 30 days,** reintroduce suspect foods one per meal. Before eating the food, take your resting pulse. Twenty minutes after eating, take your pulse again.

If your pulse after eating is 10 beats or more per minute faster than your pulse before eating, you may be sensitive to the food you've just reintroduced. Avoid the food for another 30 days.

If you remain sensitive to this food for several months, eliminate it permanently.

NUTRITIONAL SUPPLEMENTS

Headaches occur less frequently in individuals whose intake of certain key nutrients is adequate. *Ask your doctor about taking...*

•**Magnesium** (400 milligrams [mg] a day). This mineral has no effect on tension headaches but is moderately effective against migraines and cluster headaches.

Most effective: Slow-release or chelated magnesium tablets. They're better absorbed than conventional tablets.

•**Fish oil or flaxseed oil** (15 grams [g] per day). These oils are rich in omega-3 fatty acids, which have been associated with reduced migraine frequency and severity.

•**Lecithin** (200 mg a day). This protein—sold as a powder that can be mixed into beverages—reduces symptoms of cluster headaches.

•**Vitamin B-2** (riboflavin). Megadoses of this B vitamin—400 mg a day for two to three months—have been shown to reduce the frequency and severity of migraines.

Megadoses should be taken only under a doctor's supervision.

ACUPUNCTURE

Acupuncture works against tension and migraine headaches. Typically, the patient undergoes weekly or twice-weekly sessions for 10 weeks, followed by monthly "maintenance" sessions.

For the name of an acupuncturist in your area, contact the American Academy of Medical Acupuncture at 323-937-5514, *www.medicalacupuncture.org.*

Caution: Make sure the acupuncturist uses disposable needles.

In many cases, headaches can be prevented via acupressure, the self-help variant of acupuncture. *Try the following techniques at the first sign of pain...*

●**Press your thumbs against the hollows between the muscles in the neck**—just below the base of the skull and in line with your ears. Hold for two minutes. Breathe deeply throughout.

●**Use your thumbs to press the upper inside corners of the eye sockets.** Hold for one minute while breathing deeply.

●**Use your right thumb to press on the top of the fleshy mound between your left thumb and index finger.** Hold for one minute while breathing deeply. Switch hands and repeat.

ENVIRONMENTAL FACTORS

To avoid the eyestrain that triggers some headaches, be sure to have adequate lighting for the task at hand.

Trap: Fluorescent bulbs often produce a barely perceptible flicker that can cause headaches. If there's a chance fluorescent flicker is behind your headaches, switch to incandescent bulbs.

Important: Have a professional eye exam once a year. Straining to compensate for poor vision can cause headaches.

Mold, dust mites and fungi can also trigger headaches. To eliminate these airborne irritants, install exhaust fans in your bathrooms and kitchen...and a dehumidifier in your basement or any other damp area. Indoor humidity should stay between 35% and 40%.

Use scent-free hypoallergenic soap and nonaerosol sprays.

Some headaches are triggered by chronic low-level exposure to carbon monoxide (CO). Never leave a car idling in an attached garage. Consider installing a CO detector in your home.

HERBAL REMEDIES

Feverfew can reduce the frequency and severity of migraines. If you would like to try this herb, chew two fresh or freeze-dried leaves a day...or take 125 mg of dried feverfew that contains at least 0.2% parthenolide.

There's no evidence that herbal remedies are effective for tension or cluster headaches.

MASSAGE THERAPY

Massage has been found to reduce pain caused by tension and migraine headaches—but not cluster headaches.

For referral to a massage therapist in your area, contact the American Massage Therapy Association at 877-905-2700, *www.amtamassage.org.*

BIOFEEDBACK

By using devices that measure muscle tension and blood flow, biofeedback teaches you to relax tense muscles...and boost blood flow to your scalp. Each technique can ease headache pain.

For adults, 10 or more 30- to 60-minute sessions may be necessary. Children typically need only five or six.

To find a biofeedback therapist in your area, send a self-addressed, stamped, business-sized envelope to the Biofeedback Certification Institute of America, 10200 W. 44th Ave., Suite 310, Wheat Ridge, Colorado 80033, or contact it at 303-420-2902, *www.bcia.org.*

EXERCISE

Aerobic activity is beneficial for people with chronic headaches. Adding a *mantra*—a word repeated over and over to focus the mind—enhances the effect.

Caution: Exercising during a headache tends to intensify the pain.

FOR PERSISTENT HEADACHES

If nondrug therapies fail to work within three months, consult a headache specialist.

For a list of specialists in your area, contact the National Headache Foundation (NHF) at 888-643-5552, *www.headaches.org*...or send a self-addressed, stamped, business-sized envelope to the NHF at 820 N. Orleans, Suite 217, Chicago 60610.

Best Pain Relievers for Arthritis, Backaches, Headaches, More

Jacob Teitelbaum, MD, director of The Annapolis Center for Effective CFS/Fibromyalgia Therapies, in Maryland. For 25 years, he has researched ways to relieve pain. He is author of *Pain Free 1-2-3!* (Deva) and *From Fatigued to Fantastic!* (Avery). *www.endfatigue.com.*

Most of us turn to acetaminophen (Tylenol) and ibuprofen (Advil, Motrin) for pain relief—but there can be more effective approaches, including combining conventional and natural pain relievers.

Caution: Check with your doctor before taking any new medication or supplement.

ARTHRITIS

There are two types of arthritis—osteoarthritis, in which cartilage between bones wears away... and rheumatoid arthritis, an autoimmune disease that inflames joints. For relief, people with either type often take nonsteroidal anti-inflammatory drugs (NSAIDs), such as aspirin, ibuprofen and naproxen (Aleve, Naprosyn)—but 16,000 Americans die annually from side effects of these drugs. Another estimated 55,000 died from taking the recently recalled Vioxx, Bextra and other Cox-2 inhibitors (a class of NSAIDs). *Instead, try...*

●**For osteoarthritis...**

●Glucosamine sulfate. Take 1,500 milligrams (mg) of this supplement—made from chitin, which is derived from shellfish—with 3 grams (g) a day of *methylsulfonylmethane* (MSM), a natural substance in the human body. These nutrients repair cartilage, reducing arthritis pain within six weeks. For maximum tissue repair, take these supplements for two to five months. For chronic arthritis, you may continue for up to a year.

●Lidoderm. Put a patch, available by prescription, on the joint. It contains the anesthetics Novocain and Lidocaine. Wear it for about 12 hours a day (one patch lasts that long) for two to six weeks. For a large area, some people may use as many as four patches (the package says three). Many patients experience a 30% to 50% decrease in pain within two weeks.

●Willow bark and Boswellia. These herbs are as effective as Vioxx and Motrin. Take 240 milligrams (mg) of willow bark and 1,000 mg of Boswellia daily. It can take six weeks to work. For chronic arthritis, you may need to take these for up to a year to feel the full effect.

●**For rheumatoid arthritis...**

●Fish oil. Studies show that fish oil (one to two tablespoons a day for at least three months) can reduce inflammation and pain. Eskimo-3, available at health-food stores, and Nordic Naturals (800-662-2544, *www.nordicnaturals.com*) don't have the high levels of mercury that may be present in other brands. Keep taking the fish oil after the pain is gone as a preventive measure.

BACK PAIN

Back pain can occur for no apparent reason and at any point on your spine. *For relief, try...*

●**Lidoderm.** For low back pain, apply a Lidoderm patch in the morning and remove it in the evening. Expect relief in two to six weeks.

●**Colchicine.** About 70% of back pain can be eliminated without surgery, with six intravenous injections of the gout medicine *colchicine*. It enters the space between the discs of the vertebrae and reduces inflammation. Colchicine's main risk is a rare but severe allergic reaction (similar to that caused by penicillin).

CARPAL TUNNEL SYNDROME

When a nerve passing under a ligament through two bones in the wrist becomes swollen and pinched, it causes pain, numbness and tingling in the hand or forearm. *For relief, try...*

●**Vitamin B6 and thyroid hormone.** Take 250 mg a day of B6. Also ask your doctor about a prescription for natural thyroid hormone. The combination of B6 and thyroid hormone decreases swelling and usually clears up the problem after six to 12 weeks. You can stay on this treatment for six months to prevent a recurrence. During treatment, wear a wrist splint at night and, if possible, during the day.

HEADACHES

Tension headaches begin and end gradually. They can last for minutes or sometimes hours. The pain comes from tightened muscles across the forehead and/or at the base of the skull.

●**Ultram** (*tramadol hydrochloride*) is an often-overlooked but effective prescription pain reliever. Take up to 100 mg as many as four times a day.

Migraines—severe headaches that may be preceded by lights flashing before your eyes and accompanied by nausea, vomiting, sweating and dizziness—can last for hours, even days. *Natural remedies are more effective than prescription drugs at preventing migraines...*

•**Butterbur,** from the butterbur plant, can prevent—and even eliminate—migraines. Take 50 mg three times a day for one month, then one 50-mg dose twice a day to prevent attacks. Take 100 mg every three hours to eliminate an acute migraine. Use only high-quality brands, such as Enzymatic Therapy (800-783-2286, *www.enzy.com*) and Integrative Therapeutics' Petadolex (800-931-1709, *www.integrativeinc.com*).

•**Sumatriptan (Imitrex).** When a migraine is developing, 75% of patients experience tenderness and pain around the eyes. Sumatriptan knocks out 93% of migraines when taken before the pain around the eyes occurs. When it is taken later, it helps in only 13% of cases. Therefore, if you have a migraine, it is best to take sumatriptan within the first five to 20 minutes.

•**Magnesium.** In the doctor's office or the hospital emergency room, intravenous magnesium can eliminate a migraine in five minutes.

IRRITABLE BOWEL SYNDROME

Irritable bowel syndrome (IBS), also known as spastic colon, is a digestive disorder characterized by bloating, abdominal cramps and diarrhea and/or constipation. *Consider...*

•**Peppermint oil.** For symptomatic relief, take one or two enteric-coated peppermint oil capsules three times a day. Peppermint oil decreases spasms of the bowel muscles. Effective brands include Enzymatic Therapy and Mentharil, available at most health-food stores.

•**Hyoscyamine (Anaspaz, Levsin).** Take this prescription antispasmodic as needed. It relaxes the muscular contractions of the stomach and intestines. Dosages range from 0.125 to 0.375 mg, taken 30 to 60 minutes before a meal.

SHINGLES

This itchy, blistering rash—from *herpes zoster*, the virus associated with chicken pox—strikes in middle or old age and usually afflicts one side of the upper body. The virus affects the nerves, so it can leave victims in chronic pain, a condition called postherpetic neuralgia (PHN). *Discuss these options with your doctor...*

•**Ketamine.** This prescription anesthetic can decrease shingles pain within days in 65% of

cases. Apply a gel of 5% ketamine to the painful area two to three times daily.

•**Lidoderm.** Place a patch over the area of maximum pain.

•**Neurontin.** This prescription medication also can reduce pain. To avoid side effects, start with 100 to 300 mg, one to four times a day.

•**Tricyclic antidepressant.** A prescription tricyclic such as *amitriptyline* (Elavil) can relieve nerve pain. To avoid side effects, use a low dose of 10 to 50 mg.

Breakthrough Treatments For Arthritis

Harris H. McIlwain, MD, a specialist in pain-related diseases, practices with the Tampa Medical Group, Tampa, FL. Board-certified in rheumatology and geriatric medicine, he is coauthor of *Pain-Free Arthritis: A 7-Step Program for Feeling Better Again.* Owl.

If you have arthritis, chances are you have a well-worn heating pad and a medicine cabinet full of painkillers. Unfortunately, these approaches offer only temporary relief for both osteoarthritis (an age-related disease that causes joint pain and stiffness) and rheumatoid arthritis (an autoimmune disease that causes joint inflammation).

Even though there's no cure for arthritis, several underutilized treatments can dramatically curb your symptoms...

EXERCISE

Arthritis patients often avoid exercise, fearing it will exacerbate muscle and joint pain. Yet research consistently shows that exercise alleviates arthritis symptoms and improves strength and flexibility. Exercise also helps prevent weight gain, which has been shown to worsen arthritis pain.

Scientific evidence: Researchers at Wake Forest University School of Medicine found that aerobic or resistance exercise reduces the incidence of disability for key daily activities (eating, dressing, bathing, etc.) in arthritis patients by about 50%.

What to do: Stretch at least 10 minutes daily. Perform an aerobic activity, such as biking or walking, gradually working up to 30 minutes, five days a week. Do strengthening exercises, such as resistance machines or weight lifting, gradually working up to 15 minutes, three times a week.*

To minimize pain and prevent injury, apply warm, moist heat to arthritic joints or sore muscles for 15 minutes before and after exercise.

BOOST YOUR C AND D

Vitamin C is believed to slow the loss of cartilage due to osteoarthritis, while a diet low in vitamin D may speed the progression of osteoarthritis.

Scientific evidence: In research conducted as part of the ongoing Framingham Heart Study, doctors discovered that patients who ate a diet high in vitamin D, or took D supplements, reduced their risk for worsening arthritis by 75%. A study of 25,000 people by the Arthritis Research Campaign in England found that a low intake of vitamin C may increase the risk of developing arthritis.

What to do: Take daily supplements that provide 500 to 1,000 milligrams (mg) of vitamin C and 400 international units (IU) of vitamin D.

DRINK TEA

Tea may help reduce arthritis inflammation and bone deterioration.

Scientific evidence: Researchers recently discovered that green tea contains a *polyphenol*, or chemical compound, that suppresses the expression of a key gene involved in arthritis inflammation. Black tea is made of the same leaves and may be as beneficial, even though it is processed differently.

What to do: Drink one to two cups of hot or cold tea daily.

EAT GRAPES

Grape skins contain *resveratrol*, the only natural compound known to act as a Cox-2 inhibitor. Like *celecoxib* (Celebrex), resveratrol both suppresses the Cox-2 gene and deactivates the Cox-2 enzyme, which produces inflammation at the site of injury or pain.

Scientific evidence: A study published in the *Journal of Biological Chemistry* confirmed that resveratrol acts as an antioxidant and a Cox-2 inhibitor.

*A physician or physical therapist can help you to devise a safe movement program that combines stretching, aerobic and strengthening exercises.

What to do: Eat one cup of white or red grapes daily.

Good news: Imbibing your grapes may be as healthful as munching them. All wines have some resveratrol, with red wine packing the biggest punch.

TRY SUPPLEMENTS

Dietary supplements can be a valuable adjunct to traditional drug treatments, allowing patients to reduce or, in some cases, eliminate expensive medications.* *The most effective are...*

•**Glucosamine.** Derived from the shells of shellfish, this supplement appears to help lubricate joints and reduce arthritis pain and stiffness.

Scientific evidence: In a *British Medical Journal* report, 1,500 mg of glucosamine daily was found to slow cartilage deterioration in patients with osteoarthritis.

What to do: Ask your doctor about taking 1,500 mg of glucosamine daily. Glucosamine is often packaged with chondroitin, but there is less evidence to support the effectiveness of chondroitin.

Warning: People who have shellfish allergies should *not* take glucosamine.

•**SAM-e** (*S-adenosylmethionine*). Doctors in Europe commonly prescribe this natural supplement for depression and arthritis.

Scientific evidence: Studies show it relieves pain and inflammation about as well as *naproxen* (Aleve), but without the stomach upset and other side effects. It has the added benefit of boosting mood, possibly by increasing production of the brain chemical *dopamine*.

What to do: If your arthritis does not improve with glucosamine, ask your doctor about taking 400 to 1,200 mg of SAM-e daily.

GET A MASSAGE

Manual manipulation by physical or massage therapists is among the most effective treatments known for relieving neck and back pain.

Scientific evidence: In a study reported in the *Archives of Internal Medicine*, back pain patients who underwent 10 weeks of therapeutic massage took fewer medications the following year than did patients who were not massaged.

*Always consult your doctor before taking supplements. Some may interfere with the action or efficacy of certain drugs.

What to do: Consider getting regular massages, as needed, for pain.

Whenever possible, choose a state licensed massage therapist. To find one, contact the American Massage Therapy Association, 877-905-2700, *www.amtamassage.org.*

CONSIDER THERAPEUTIC TAPING

Therapeutic taping—in which rigid tape is wrapped around a joint to realign, support and take pressure from it—may have significant pain relief benefits for some osteoarthritis patients.

Scientific evidence: In an Australian study, 73% of patients with osteoarthritis of the knee experienced substantially reduced symptoms after three weeks of therapeutic taping. The benefits were comparable with those achieved with standard drug treatments and lasted three weeks after taping was stopped. Though the study looked only at knees, taping may work as well for elbows, wrists and ankles.

What to do: Ask your doctor if therapeutic taping is right for you.

Important: Taping must be done properly to be effective. If you try taping, you should have your sore joint wrapped by a physician or physical therapist who is familiar with the procedure. He/she can show you or a family member the proper technique.

If taping proves too difficult or cumbersome, a fitted neoprene sleeve (an elastic sleeve used by athletes) may offer similar benefits. It's available at most drugstores.

PAIN RELIEF STRATEGIES

To minimize your arthritis pain and protect your joints...

•**When grocery shopping,** request plastic bags that can be looped over your arms, between the wrist and elbow. This shifts the weight to your shoulders and upper body, instead of the more delicate wrist and hand joints.

•**Put foam "grips" around pens and pencils** (you'll find them in office supply stores). You can use these same covers around crochet hooks and knitting needles, too.

•**Use pump toothpastes** rather than the traditional squeeze tubes.

•**Choose clothing with Velcro closures** instead of zippers and buttons.

•**Women should wear the type of bra** that opens in the front.

All About the Amazing Power of Acupuncture

Gary Kaplan, DO, associate professor of community and family medicine, Georgetown University School of Medicine, Washington, DC, and past president, Medical Acupuncture Research Foundation. He is founder and owner of the Kaplan Clinic, Arlington, VA, which integrates conventional and family medicine with complementary approaches, such as acupuncture, osteopathic manipulative therapy, homeopathy, nutritional remedies and mind–body medicine. *www.kaplanclinic.com.*

A cupuncture is no longer a "fringe" treatment. Since 1997, when it was formally recognized as a legitimate medical technique,* acupuncture's uses in Western medicine have been growing. *Here's what it can do for you...*

HOW IT WORKS

Acupuncture involves the insertion of hair-thin needles into one or more of the body's 2,000-plus acupuncture points. In traditional Chinese medicine, it's thought that the needles rebalance the flow of energy (*chi*) through 14 major pathways, or meridians. Acupuncture used to be considered questionable because meridians couldn't be readily identified.

Fact: Acupuncture points do exist. Each one is located near a vascular bundle that contains a nerve, artery, vein and lymphatic vessel in the space between muscles. The effects of stimulating specific points have been scientifically verified.

Example: One acupuncture point on the foot has traditionally been linked to eye disorders. Brain scans performed at the University of California, Irvine, showed that stimulating that point increased activity in the brain's occipital region, the area involved with vision.

Acupuncture therapy usually involves a series of six to 12 treatments over a period of weeks or months. The cost per treatment is $45 to $150, with the average around $90. It sometimes is covered by insurance.

It used to be thought that acupuncture provided only short-term relief. In some cases, however, acupuncture appears to permanently alter the way cells function—for example, increasing the ability of nerve cells to release painkilling neurotransmitters. This shows promise for the treatment of

*By the National Institutes of Health Consensus Development Conference.

chronic conditions such as osteoarthritis, tendinitis, headaches and irritable bowel syndrome.

The World Health Organization has identified more than 40 conditions that may be helped by acupuncture. *The best evidence is for the following conditions...*

BACK PAIN

Many physicians routinely recommend acupuncture for low-back pain, and insurance companies often pay for it. Acupuncture works at least as well as over-the-counter drugs—without causing stomach upset or other side effects.

Acupuncture appears to increase blood supply to injured areas and promote faster healing. It also may encourage the release of painkilling endorphins and stimulate nerve fibers to block pain sensations. Patients with acute back sprains or spasms who are treated with acupuncture in addition to conventional treatments (ice packs, massage, physical therapy, etc.) can cut their healing time in half, from an average of about four weeks to two.

TOOTH EXTRACTION

Patients who have teeth extracted or other oral surgeries experience less postsurgical pain and require lower doses of analgesics when given acupuncture afterward. They also have less swelling and inflammation. In addition to causing an increase in painkilling endorphins, acupuncture lowers levels of *prostaglandins*, inflammatory chemicals that cause nerve and tissue irritation.

SURGICAL PAIN

Studies have shown that patients given acupuncture during surgery require lower levels of anesthesia—and have fewer anesthesia-related complications such as nausea. Acupuncture also can be used postsurgically to help control pain.

NAUSEA AND VOMITING

More than three dozen randomized controlled studies have shown that acupuncture is effective for treating and preventing nausea and vomiting—important for cancer patients getting chemotherapy. A study of 104 women undergoing high-dose chemotherapy found that those given acupuncture had significantly less nausea and vomiting than those who didn't get the treatments. Acupuncture also may be helpful for reducing morning sickness during pregnancy.

PAINFUL MENSTRUATION

A number of studies have shown that women with dysmenorrhea (painful menstrual periods) can get long-lasting relief with acupuncture. In a typical case, a woman might receive several treatments prior to her period, then additional treatments afterward. A total of six to 12 treatments can potentially eliminate the problem for good.

The uterine contractions that result in menstrual cramps are caused by an upsurge in prostaglandins. Acupuncture can calm the nervous system and potentially cause a permanent reduction in prostaglandins.

ADDICTION

Acupuncture has been used to treat just about every form of addiction—tobacco, alcohol, heroin, etc. It may reduce physical and emotional withdrawal when combined with conventional approaches, such as psychotherapy and medication.

Example: Studies have shown that about 60% of addicts drop out of traditional treatment programs, but the dropout rate declines to approximately 40% when acupuncture is included.

ACUPUNCTURE SAFETY

To get proper treatment...

•**Get a diagnosis from a medical doctor** before getting acupuncture treatments. Otherwise you might be misdiagnosed.

Example: My brother-in-law had a high fever and went to an acupuncturist, who treated him for flu and a urinary tract infection. What he really had was prostatitis with early sepsis, a potentially life-threatening infection that required antibiotic treatment.

•**See a qualified acupuncturist**—either a medical acupuncturist (MD or DO), a practitioner who is a member of the American Academy of Medical Acupuncture (AAMA, 323-937-5514, *www.medicalacupuncture.org*) or one who is board-certified by the American Board of Medical Acupuncture, an independent entity within the AAMA...or a licensed acupuncturist, a practitioner who has completed the state or national exams conducted by the National Certification Commission for Acupuncture and Oriental Medicine (NCCAOM, 703-548-9004, *www.nccaom.org*).

•**Ask how many treatments will be needed.** If it's more than 12 or the practitioner won't be specific, get a second opinion.

•**Avoid acupuncture if you are taking anticoagulant medications** such as *coumadin* or *heparin*, or if you have a bleeding disorder such as hemophilia.

Folk Remedies that Really Work

Earl Mindell, PhD, RPh, professor of nutrition at Pacific Western University, Los Angeles, and an expert on nutrition, drugs, vitamins and herbal remedies. He is author of *Natural Remedies for 101 Ailments* (Basic Health) and *Earl Mindell's Vitamin Bible for the 21st Century* (Warner).

Physicians often dismiss folk cures as quaint, ineffective or potentially unsafe. But, that could be a mistake.

Research has found that some traditional remedies work as well as—or even better than—drugs. What's more, most of these traditional treatments are safer than drugs because they rarely cause side effects or interact with other medical treatments.

Best folk cures…*

COLDS

There's a good reason that mothers have long recommended chicken soup as a cold remedy. Studies have confirmed that chicken soup increases the activity of antiviral immune cells and also reduces throat and sinus inflammation.

What to do: Eat a bowl of chicken soup twice daily at the first sign of a cold.

Helpful: Add a pinch of cayenne to chicken soup. *Capsaicin*, the chemical that makes cayenne and other peppers taste hot, reduces congestion as effectively as over-the-counter (OTC) medications.

HEADACHES

Most headaches are caused by muscle tension and/or emotional stress. Millions of Americans can't take aspirin or other painkillers because of drug interactions or side effects, such as stomach irritation.

What to do: Using your thumb and forefinger, squeeze the area between your upper lip and nose for five seconds. Repeat as needed. This

*Check with your doctor before trying these remedies. Herbs can be dangerous for some people, including pregnant or breast-feeding women.

technique blocks nerve signals and reduces headache pain in many sufferers.

INSOMNIA

Sleeping pills can be addictive and are notorious for side effects, such as dizziness, depression and headache.

What to do: Drink a cup of valerian tea at bedtime. Valerian root, available in tea bags at health-food stores, contains *valepotriates* and other sleep-inducing compounds. A traditional remedy for anxiety as well as sleeplessness, valerian root is recommended by Commission E, the European equivalent of the FDA.

Chamomile, hops and lavender teas will also help you rest, but they are not as potent as valerian root.

NAUSEA

Ginger is the best remedy for all forms of nausea, including motion and morning sickness. The active ingredients, *gingerols*, are more effective than OTC antinausea drugs.

What to do: Each day you have nausea, drink two to three cups of ginger ale that contains natural ginger. This variety is available at health-food stores. The ginger-flavored ingredients in commercial brands of ginger ale won't have the same effect.

As an alternative, make ginger tea. To prepare, chop about one tablespoon of fresh gingerroot and steep it in hot water for about 10 minutes. Drink one to three cups daily.

SORE THROATS

Most people have heard that gargling with warm salt water reduces sore throat pain. However, few prepare and use the mixture properly.

What to do: Add three teaspoons of table salt to one cup of warm water and stir. Gargle with a full one-cup mixture at least two to three times daily. Viruses, which cause colds, can't survive in a high-salt environment.

TOOTHACHES

Conventional treatments for toothaches range from OTC products, such as Orajel, to powerful prescription painkillers. But one of the best treatments is a generations-old folk remedy.

What to do: Dip a toothpick in oil of clove, available at health-food stores and some pharmacies, and apply it to the sore area. The pain will disappear almost instantly. Reapply as needed. If pain persists for more than a few days, see a dentist.

Scents to Boost Energy, Mood, Memory and More

Alan Hirsch, MD, founder and neurologic director, The Smell & Taste Treatment and Research Foundation, Ltd., 845 N. Michigan Ave., Chicago 60611, *www.scienceofsmell.com.*

Scents stimulate important mental and physical functions. They often trigger the release of neurotransmitters, chemicals that send signals to the brain. *What scents can do for you...*

CONTROL APPETITE

In a study of 105 people, we found that those who inhaled a chocolate-like aroma whenever they felt like eating lost nearly three pounds in two weeks. A study of 3,193 volunteers found that sniffing banana, green apple or peppermint scents resulted in an average weight loss of 30 pounds in six months.

Sniff the above scents often, and smell every food before you eat it. Your brain will perceive that you're eating more, thus suppressing your appetite.

INCREASE ENERGY

These odors stimulate the part of the brain that promotes wakefulness...

• **Jasmine** causes an increase in beta waves in the brain, a sign of alertness. Jasmine tea is a great pick-me-up.

• **Strawberries and buttered popcorn** cause exercisers to burn more calories.

• **Peppermint** works on sensory nerves and increases alertness. Try it as candy or gum.

• **Freshly brewed coffee** is very stimulating, probably because we associate the aroma with the energizing effects of caffeine.

BOOST ROMANCE

Both men and women are sexually stimulated by scents, but the odors that arouse them aren't the same.

For men: The smell of lavender or pumpkin pie increases blood flow to the penis by about 40%. The smell of doughnuts, black licorice, vanilla and women's perfume (any scent) also are sexually stimulating to men.

For women: The odors of cucumber and licorice are stimulating. Women are turned off by the smell of cherries, barbecued meat and men's cologne.

REDUCE ANXIETY

Fresh, natural scents, in general, induce calm. In a study we conducted, volunteers became extremely anxious when put in coffin-like tubes —but then calmed down when the tubes were infused with the smells of green apple and cucumber. These odors act on the limbic system, the emotional center of the brain.

If you anticipate a situation in which you will feel anxious, wash your hair that morning with a green apple–scented shampoo and/or put a dab of the shampoo in a cloth to take with you.

IMPROVE MEMORY

People who sniff floral scents increase their retention of new material by 17%.

Sniff a floral odor when learning new material, then smell it again when you want to recall it. This is known as *state-dependent learning.* The material you learn in one state—while smelling roses—will be more accessible when you replicate that state in the future.

Surprising Causes of Memory Problems...and What to Do About Them

Majid Fotuhi, MD, PhD, assistant professor of neurology, Johns Hopkins University School of Medicine, and director, Memory Disorders Unit, Sinai Hospital, both in Baltimore. He is author of *The Memory Cure: How to Protect Your Brain Against Memory Loss and Alzheimer's Disease.* McGraw-Hill. His PBS special, *Conquering Memory Loss,* is available on DVD and VHS.

Everyone forgets things sometimes. Though many people believe that memory loss is an early sign of Alzheimer's disease, more than 90% of those who complain about poor memory don't have Alzheimer's.

If it's not Alzheimer's, what is it? *Common causes of memory loss and best treatments...*

DEPRESSION

This is the leading cause of memory loss. Depressed people have low brain levels of *serotonin* and *norepinephrine,* neurochemicals that normally activate the hippocampus. The hippocampus is the memory part of the brain where information is stored and retrieved.

Besides memory loss, warning signs of depression include changes in appetite and/or sleep patterns…lack of enjoyment in things that used to give pleasure…mood swings or emotional unresponsiveness…and/or frequent self-criticism.

What to do: Antidepressants such as Paxil, Prozac, Zoloft and other *selective serotonin reuptake inhibitors* (SSRIs) relieve depression in the majority of patients. Memory, concentration and other cognitive functions usually start to improve quickly, often within six weeks.

STRESS

People who experience chronic stress due to job issues, family or money worries, etc., often experience memory problems.

Stress raises levels of *cortisol*, a hormone that improves concentration briefly during acute stressful situations. However, cortisol damages the hippocampus when brain levels remain high due to continuous stress.

Even stress caused by transitory life events such as a divorce can make it hard to concentrate and absorb information. You can't retrieve information that doesn't make it into memory storage in the first place.

What to do: Take stress seriously. Your memory problems will continue to worsen if you don't control it.

Get regular exercise…practice relaxation techniques, such as deep breathing and yoga… and spend more time doing pleasurable activities to reduce stress.

POOR SLEEP

Lack of sleep increases stress and anxiety, which raises cortisol levels. Depression can cause insomnia, as can stress. Once the underlying condition is relieved, sleep usually improves.

Disturbed sleep also can be caused by obstructive sleep apnea, periodic interruptions in breathing. Some sufferers experience hundreds of "micro-awakenings" each night that prevent them from entering deep-sleep stages. Apnea warning signs include morning headaches… gasping or snorting during sleep…waking up with a dry mouth or throat…depression…excessive fatigue…high blood pressure…and bedding that's extremely rumpled.

What to do: Your doctor may recommend a treatment called *nasal continuous positive airway pressure* (nCPAP). A mask worn while sleeping creates air pressure that keeps the upper airways open, preventing apnea and snoring. Many of my patients who use nCPAP report dramatic improvements in sleep and memory almost immediately.

Most people who have sleep apnea are overweight. Fatty tissue around the upper airway sags during sleep and obstructs the normal flow of air. Apnea as well as snoring often diminish significantly when people lose as little as 10 pounds.

VITAMIN B-12 DEFICIENCY

This accounts for approximately 10% of non-Alzheimer's memory loss cases. The body uses vitamin B-12 to produce *myelin*, the sheathing on nerve cells. Low levels of this nutrient cause myelin abnormalities that slow the transmission of nerve signals. This can impair memory and other cognitive functions, especially when accompanied by ministrokes (see below) or other types of vascular problems.

Even people who consume enough vitamin B-12—found in meat, dairy, eggs and fish—may have low blood levels because they don't produce enough *intrinsic factor*, a protein secreted by stomach cells that is required for vitamin B-12 absorption.

Low intrinsic factor is seen more commonly in young people. Low B-12 levels in elderly people usually are caused by slower absorption in the gastrointestinal tract.

What to do: Doctors routinely check the blood for B-12 in those with unexplained memory problems. You'll need supplementation if levels are low. Oral B-12 isn't effective if the body isn't producing enough intrinsic factor. Most patients require monthly injections of B-12.

People who follow a strict vegan diet (no animal foods whatsoever) should supplement with six micrograms (mcg) of vitamin B-12 daily. A vegan diet doesn't affect levels of intrinsic factor, so oral supplements are effective. In general, it is a good idea for most people to take a multivitamin daily.

THYROID DISEASE

Too little or too much thyroid hormone can cause mental slowing, declines in vision and hearing and persistent memory problems. *Hyperthyroidism* (too much hormone) usually is caused by a tumor or an immune-system disorder. Symptoms may include palpitations and weight loss. *Hypothyroidism* (too little hormone) also can be caused by immune-system problems and often is associated with dry skin, hair loss and weight gain.

What to do: Talk to your doctor. Both hyper- and hypothyroidism are easy to treat with surgery or thyroid hormone supplements. Most people will experience dramatic improvements in memory and other cognitive functions when thyroid hormone is maintained at proper levels.

MINI-STROKES

These strokes are caused by a blockage of blood vessels in the brain. Most affect tiny, rice-sized areas of the brain and can cause minor (and sometimes transitory) memory loss.

Mini-strokes often are so subtle that patients can have 10 of them without serious symptoms.

Example: A healthy adult might be able to name 10 different fruits in a minute. Someone who has had a mini-stroke might be able to name only five. He/she also might walk a little more slowly than he did before and have a slightly weaker handshake.

What to do: Your doctor will recommend a brain CT scan if he/she suspects that you have had a mini-stroke. You can't reverse the damage, but you can reduce the risk of future mini-strokes (and a major stroke) by doing the same things that you would do to prevent a heart attack—maintain healthy blood pressure, stop smoking, lose weight, etc.

New Ways to Prevent and Treat Alzheimer's Disease

Gary Small, MD, director, Memory Clinic and Center on Aging, University of California, Los Angeles. He is author of *The Memory Bible: An Innovative Strategy for Keeping Your Brain Young.* Hyperion. For additional information, go to *www.aging.ucla.edu/memorybible.html.*

Recent research has revealed new strategies for preventing, treating and diagnosing Alzheimer's disease (AD). More than 4 million Americans suffer from AD, a progressive brain condition that ultimately leads to death. The older you get, the more likely it is that AD will strike. About 5% of people ages 65 to 74 have AD, and nearly 50% of those older than 85 may have the disease.

WARNING SIGNS OF ALZHEIMER'S

Consult a doctor if any of these symptoms cause you or others distress…

•**You often forget recently learned information**—names, appointments, phone numbers.

•**You forget how to perform simple tasks,** such as cooking or getting dressed.

•**You can't recall simple words and perhaps resort to descriptions,** such as "that thing you drink out of" instead of "glass."

Changes in brain function that go beyond memory can indicate AD. *These include…*

•**Confusion or agitation.**

•**Mood changes.** These may include anxiety or depression.

•**Personality changes,** such as unusual suspiciousness, anger or loss of motivation.

Steps you should take now…

EAT RIGHT

The brain, like the heart, depends on strong circulation to stay healthy. *To be safe…*

•**Choose "good" fats.** Some fats are healthful, particularly the omega-3 fatty acids in nuts and olive oil and especially in fish. Studies have found that people who eat just one serving of fish a week are 60% less likely to develop AD.

A study at Case Western Reserve University in Cleveland found that young and middle-aged adults who ate a low-fat diet had a reduced risk of AD decades later, particularly compared with those whose diets were higher in saturated fat—the kind found in meats and whole-fat dairy products.

•**Watch cholesterol.** High cholesterol, which is associated with diets high in saturated fat, has been linked to AD. In a recent clinical trial, a cholesterol-lowering statin drug reduced the incidence of AD and heart disease.

If you have high cholesterol, treat it aggressively—with statin drugs if necessary.

•**Maximize antioxidants.** Numerous fruits and vegetables contain antioxidants, such as vitamins C and E, that can neutralize the free radicals that kill brain cells. Prime sources of antioxidants include citrus fruits, berries, broccoli, carrots and tomatoes.

New study: A Johns Hopkins survey of nearly 5,000 people age 65 and older suggests that antioxidant supplements offer potent protection. The study found that those who took both vitamins C and E had about one-third the risk of AD compared with those who took neither.

Ideal daily dosage: Take 500 milligrams (mg) of vitamin C and 400 international units (IU) of vitamin E.*

•**Control calories.** Being overweight makes you more vulnerable to diabetes and high blood pressure, both of which raise the risk of AD. A recent study conducted by Utah State University also found an association between obesity and higher rates of AD, unconnected to other health problems.

•**Drink in moderation.** People who consume modest amounts of alcohol (one glass of wine, one bottle of beer or one shot of spirits daily for women…two for men) are less likely to develop AD than those who drink more or not at all.

REDUCE STRESS

Chronic stress appears to damage the parts of the brain that control memory, such as the hippocampus, and may increase the risk of AD. In one study of nearly 800 men reported in *Neurology*, those most prone to psychological distress were twice as likely to develop AD as those who were least stressed.

Ask yourself if the things that bother you really are so important. Are there sources of stress that you can modify? Also regularly practice relaxation exercises, such as meditation, deep breathing and peaceful imagery.

STAY ACTIVE

Regular aerobic exercise increases brain circulation. Physical activity also fosters connections between brain cells, maintaining healthy mental function.

Exercise reduces stress, too. A Canadian study found that just 15 to 30 minutes of brisk walking three times a week cuts the risk of AD by about one-third.

DO MENTAL AEROBICS

Any activity that challenges your mind increases the strength and stamina of brain cells. A study in *The New England Journal of Medicine* found that adults who regularly enjoyed

*Due to the possible interactions between vitamin E and various drugs and supplements as well as other safety considerations, be sure to consult your doctor before starting a vitamin E regimen.

such leisure activities as chess, board games and crossword puzzles were 63% less likely to get AD than those who did not. Expand your mind with something new. Take an adult education course, learn a new language, read a challenging book, study a musical instrument.

PROTECT YOUR HEAD

A number of studies have confirmed that a single serious concussion—an injury that causes unconsciousness for 60 minutes or longer—doubles the risk of AD later in life. Whether lesser traumas also are dangerous is uncertain. Repeated impact ("heading" a soccer ball, for example) does appear to be associated with impaired memory.

Use seat belts in the car. Wear a helmet when riding a bicycle or motorcycle, skiing, skating, etc. You even may want to wear a helmet in the car. An Australian study found that wearing a bicycle-style helmet in the car lessened the severity of brain injuries by 50% and saved the life of one in five head-injury victims.

IF ALZHEIMER'S STRIKES

A doctor will review your symptoms. He/she may order tests such as magnetic resonance imaging (MRI) to rule out other conditions that can cause similar symptoms, such as a stroke or possibly a tumor.

New: Positron emission tomography (PET) scan is a brain-imaging test that can show damage caused by AD, even in early stages. The cost ranges from $700 to $1,500.

There is no cure for AD, but modern medications can slow its progression.

Common drugs: Cholinesterase inhibitors —*donepezil* (Aricept), *galantamine* (Reminyl) and *rivastigmine* (Exelon). These block the enzyme that breaks down the brain chemical acetylcholine and may delay the progression of symptoms for up to a year.

A new drug for AD was recently approved by the Food and Drug Administration. *Memantine* (Namenda) works on the brain chemical glutamate. An excess of glutamate apparently interferes with the transmission of brain signals.

New: A combination of a cholinesterase inhibitor and memantine seems to be more effective than either drug used alone. In a recent clinical trial reported in *The Journal of the American Medical Association*, patients with moderate to severe

AD who were taking the cholinesterase inhibitor *donepezil* improved significantly when memantine was added, while those who added a placebo did not improve and in some ways worsened.

Vitamin E also may slow the progress of AD once it develops, but in much higher doses than what is recommended for prevention—around 2,000 IU daily. Only take high doses as part of a medically supervised treatment program because vitamin E can cause internal bleeding.

What You Can Do Now To Stay Healthy and Keep Out of a Nursing Home

Robert N. Butler, MD, president, International Longevity Center, New York City. He is former chairman of the department of geriatrics and adult development, Mount Sinai Medical Center, New York City, the first department of geriatrics in an American medical school. He won the Pulitzer Prize for *Why Survive? Being Old in America.* Johns Hopkins University Press.

People of a certain age get lots of sales pitches for nursing home insurance. Insurance companies assume that nearly everyone will spend time in such a facility. It's a distressing thought. Fortunately, it is a fate you can avoid.

Key: Don't wait. The sooner you start a no-nursing home plan, the better your chances of having it succeed.

GOOD NEWS ABOUT DEMENTIA

Dementia is common among nursing home residents. Not too long ago, we assumed that cognitive decline was simply a part of getting old. However, new research shows this isn't the case. *There are three specific factors that help maintain cognitive health...*

•**Daily physical activity.** This often surprises people, but the research is clear—we can actually measure that people who are active physically are stronger cognitively. When the Roman poet and satirist Juvenal said, "A healthy mind in a healthy body," he knew what he was talking about.

We recommend that people walk 10,000 steps a day to be sure they are getting enough exercise. The average person walks just 4,000 steps, so you'll probably need to establish new habits

(and buy a pedometer) to make 10,000 steps part of your everyday life.

•**Social interaction.** Being socially engaged doesn't mean that you have to maintain a full social calendar. What it does mean is that you remain involved with other people, whether through work or volunteering. For those who are retired, there are many volunteer opportunities, from your local community to the Peace Corps. And don't forget the importance of being active as a grandparent. That benefits all three generations.

•**Intellectual stimulation.** This directly impacts the brain. Many older people enjoy studying academic subjects from history to astronomy, but we have found that learning another language is particularly good for strong cognitive skills. The work that goes into mastering foreign words and an unfamiliar language structure keeps the brain's neurons firing and busy.

FITNESS FACTS

The next crucial part of a no-nursing home plan is to create and maintain very good health habits. *To start, you must practice all forms of fitness, such as...*

•**Aerobic exercise.** Aerobic exercise—the kind that gets your heart rate up and keeps it there—is a must. To maintain heart and lung stamina, perform aerobic exercise for at least 20 minutes three or more times a week.

Examples: Fast walking, jogging, swimming.

•**Strength training.** This form of fitness is often overlooked by many older people and it's incredibly important as you age.

Being strong allows you to more easily perform what are called ADLs, activities of daily living. Without strong quads—the muscles in front of the thigh—you lose the ability to get up out of a chair, go to the bathroom, sit down easily. Without strong arm muscles, you have trouble lifting bags or opening and closing windows. Strength training is crucial and you must keep it up throughout your life.

Examples: Squats, getting out of a chair without using your arms, chest presses.

•**Balance exercises.** Among older people, there are some 250,000 fractures a year and many of these fractures land the elderly in nursing homes. This is especially sad because many of the falls that cause broken bones can be prevented by improving balance. The sense of balance is like a muscle—you must exercise it regularly or it will weaken and lose its usefulness to you. The easiest way to practice balance is to stand on one leg and move the other, bent at the knee, through space. Do this several times a day. Or try standing on one leg while you brush your teeth.

Safety reminder: Be sure to have something sturdy nearby to grab hold of in case you need additional support.

•**Stretching exercises.** Finally, you must practice flexibility, which refers to the range of motion of your joints.

Range of motion becomes increasingly important as you age. If compromised, it, too, intrudes on your ability to function in your everyday life. Your shoulders need range of motion to enable you to reach for things...your hips and knees need range of motion to bend properly. Keep your joints flexible through regular stretching exercises. Try stretching your arms across your chest. Or stretch the backs of your legs by standing with the palms of your hands braced against a wall while you stretch one leg at a time behind you.

OTHER HEALTH POINTERS

•**Eat a nutritious diet.** In addition to plenty of fruits and vegetables, your diet should be low in fats and have no trans fatty acids at all. Processed baked foods virtually always contain unhealthy trans fatty acids, but you're more likely to see "partially hydrogenated fat" on the label. They are the same thing and you shouldn't eat them. Trans fats are created during the chemical process of hydrogenating oils and they increase "bad" LDL cholesterol, increasing your risk of stroke and heart disease.

•**Maintain a healthy weight.** This will help you avoid many diseases that often bring patients into a nursing home, such as type II diabetes and some cardiovascular diseases, especially high blood pressure that leads to stroke.

•**Quit smoking.** I wish I had no need to say quit smoking, but there are still people who haven't kicked the habit even though statistics show it cuts seven years off the normal life span.

Subtle Stroke Signs

The telltale symptoms of stroke include weakness or numbness on one side of the body, difficulty speaking and/or vision loss.

These symptoms often go unrecognized. In fact, only 25% of stroke victims know they're having a stroke.

If you notice suspicious symptoms, seek immediate medical attention. If you wait, you may be unable to benefit from new "clot-busting" drugs, which minimize brain damage.

Linda S. Williams, MD, assistant professor of neurology, Indiana University School of Medicine, Indianapolis. Her study of 67 stroke patients was published in *Stroke.*

Stroke Stopper

An FDA-approved device removes blood clots in people experiencing a stroke. The *mechanical embolus removal in cerebral ischemia* (MERCI) retriever is threaded up from the groin into the affected artery and used like a corkscrew to pluck out the clot. It can be used up to eight hours after stroke onset. The intravenous drug tissue plasminogen activator (tPA) can dissolve clots, but it can't be used more than three hours after stroke onset...or in patients with bleeding disorders or who have had surgery recently.

Gary Duckwiler, MD, president, American Society of Interventional and Therapeutic Neuroradiology (ASITN), Fairfax, VA, and professor of radiology, University of California, Los Angeles.

Good for the Heart ...and More

Beans have even more antioxidants than blueberries, commonly thought to have the most antioxidants. One-half cup of dried small red beans has more antioxidant capacity than one full cup of wild blueberries. Red kidney beans have almost as much antioxidant capacity as wild blueberries...followed by pinto beans, cultivated blueberries and cranberries.

Ronald Prior, PhD, research chemist and nutritionist, US Department of Agriculture's Arkansas Children's Nutrition Center, Little Rock, and leader of a study of 100 different types of fruits, vegetables, berries, nuts and spices, published in *Journal of Agricultural and Food Chemistry.*

Heart Doctor's Stop-Smoking Plan

Most people need a strategy to quit smoking. *Following is one heart doctor's suggestions...*

•**Write down the day you will quit**—between two and four weeks from the day you decide—and keep the date in sight.

•**Pick a nonworking day to quit**—to limit stress.

•**For seven days, record every cigarette smoked.** Number each, and write when you smoked it and why.

•**See which cigarettes you smoked from habit and boredom,** and drop them first. Work toward dropping the harder ones.

•**Start walking or bike riding regularly.** Fight smoking urges by brushing your hair or playing with a rubber band.

•**Take it one day at a time**—most withdrawal symptoms end within four weeks.

Mary McGowan, MD, director, Cholesterol Management Center, New England Heart Institute, Manchester, NH and author of *Heart Fitness for Life: The Essential Guide to Preventing and Reversing Heart Disease.* Oxford University Press.

Weight-Loss Secret

You can lose five pounds a year just by drinking two liters of water a day. Drinking water speeds your metabolism—in fact, you start to burn fat after you drink just two glasses.

Jens Jordan, MD, professor of clinical pharmacology and medicine, Franz-Volhard Clinical Research Center, Berlin, Germany, and leader of a study published in *Journal of Clinical Endocrinology & Metabolism.*

Very Effective Weight-Loss Strategies

Stephen Gullo, PhD, president, Institute for Health and Weight Sciences, 16 E. 65 St., New York City 10021, and author of *Thin Tastes Better: Control Your Food Triggers Without Feeling Deprived.* Dell.

It's difficult to stay on your diet when you are in certain situations. *Here are some suggestions on how to master them...*

•**Restaurants.** Avoid the *10-minute* problems—the first 10 minutes with the bread basket staring at you and the last 10 minutes with dessert.

Skip breads altogether: Have a tomato juice or shrimp cocktail instead. For dessert, have sorbet...fruit...or cappuccino with skim milk.

Best: Have an apple...low-fat yogurt...or some other healthful snack before you go out.

•**Travel.** Do not eat desserts until the last day of your trip. If you eat them earlier, you are likely to do it throughout the entire trip.

Airports: Stay away from newsstands—they stock high-sugar snacks.

Better: Bring your own fruit.

•**Watching TV.** Don't snack in front of the TV—sip hot or cool liquids instead.

Effective strategies wherever you are: Resist cravings for 10 minutes—they may go away.

Also: Avoid going longer than three or four hours without a healthful snack or meal. Eating at regular intervals will keep your blood sugar stable and keep cravings at bay.

10,000 Steps to a Better Life

Robert N. Butler, MD, president, International Longevity Center, New York City. He is former chairman of the department of geriatrics and adult development, Mount Sinai Medical Center, New York City, the first department of geriatrics in an American medical school. He won the Pulitzer Prize for *Why Survive? Being Old in America.* Johns Hopkins University Press.

When I lived in Washington, DC, in the 1960s, I began participating in one of the most effective and enjoyable forms of exercise I know. Early each morning, a friend and I met for a fast, invigorating walk.

I didn't have to take lessons or join a gym, and it was a great way to start the day. Those early morning walks were the beginning of a valuable lifelong habit.

MIRACULOUS BENEFITS

Walking for exercise has a long tradition. Thomas Jefferson, who lived to be 83 at a time when average life expectancy was about 40, walked four miles every day. He wrote that the purpose of walking was to "relax the mind."

Now we know that walking briskly for 30 to 60 minutes each day also can help people live longer, healthier lives. Fast walking burns about the same amount of calories per mile as running, and it doesn't pound the joints. It builds endurance, enhances muscle tone and flexibility and strengthens bones. It also helps prevent heart disease, hypertension and diabetes.

In a study of Harvard graduates, the Mayo Clinic discovered that men who burned 2,000 or more calories a week by walking lived an average of one to two years longer than those who burned fewer than 500 calories a week walking.

GETTING STARTED

The only equipment a walker needs is a comfortable pair of canvas or leather shoes designed specifically for walking.

I've found it helpful to do simple stretching exercises before and after a walk.

Example: I raise my left leg on a tabletop, pointing my toes toward the ceiling. I hold the position for a minute. Then I repeat the stretch with my right leg. If a table is too high, use a chair or sofa.

Some people prefer to walk on a treadmill. Or you may choose to take advantage of day-to-day opportunities to increase your walking.

Examples: Walking up flights of stairs instead of riding the escalator or elevator…parking far away from store entrances…or even walking to the store.

The rule of thumb when you're walking is to break a sweat. Aim to reach your target heart rate (THR).

To determine THR: Subtract your age from 220. Multiply by 0.8 (80%).

10,000 STEPS

Jefferson shipped from Paris to his home in Virginia a cumbersome device that accurately counted every step he took. Today, we have a more portable version known as a pedometer, which can be clipped to a belt or waistband to count the number of steps taken. In fact, "steps per day" has become a standard unit of exercise measurement. Studies here and in Japan show that the average person needs to take at least 10,000 steps per day—what you would do in a strenuous 30-minute workout—to get maximum health benefits. At the International Longevity Center, we sell a pedometer (212-288-1468, *www.ilcusa.org*). Pedometers also are available at sporting-goods stores.

WALKING GROUPS

In recent years, hundreds of walking clubs have sprung up nationwide. You can find them by going on-line and typing "walking clubs" into a search engine.

Example: American Volkssport Association has 350 walking clubs. Go to *www.ava.org* or call 800-830-9255.

Since my return to New York City in 1982, I have walked with a group of early risers on weekends. (During the week, I walk on my own.) We get together around 7:30 am, take a brisk turn around a six-mile trail in Central Park and then enjoy a leisurely, healthy breakfast. Old friends and new get to meet and support each other's efforts to stay healthy. I credit my walking buddies with helping me reach my goal of 10,000 steps a day.

A Stronger Body in Only 30 Minutes a Week

Fredrick Hahn, president and cofounder of the National Council for Exercise Standards, an organization of exercise, medical and scientific professionals. He is owner of Serious Strength Inc., a Slow Burn strength-training studio in New York City, *www.seriousstrength.com*, and coauthor of *The Slow Burn Fitness Revolution.* Broadway.

We know the benefits of strength training. It restores muscle…increases bone density…improves balance, decreasing the likelihood of falls…and promotes weight loss and cardiovascular fitness. However, conventional strength training requires several hours a week and frequently causes injury to muscles and joints.

New, better way: The *Slow Burn* technique, in which weights are lifted and lowered with incredible slowness—about 10 seconds up and 10 seconds down. *The benefits...*

●**It's safer.** Slow lifting reduces injury-causing stress on ligaments, tendons and joints. This means that even the elderly can do it safely.

●**It's more effective.** Without the aid of momentum, more muscle fibers are exercised with each movement.

●**It's more efficient.** You can get a complete workout in 30 minutes each week—compared with at least three hours for conventional lifting.

HOW TO DO IT

In a Slow Burn workout, you complete a set of three to six repetitions of each exercise in 60 to 90 seconds. If you perform 10 exercises, you can complete your workout in approximately 10 to 15 minutes. Two workouts a week are all you will need.

To get the best results, raise and lower weights at the rate of about one inch per second. Allow a total of about 100 seconds for all repetitions of each exercise—push-ups, leg curls, etc. Breathe normally while performing each exercise.

Helpful: Use a metronome to maintain the one-inch-per-second rhythm.

Repeat each exercise until the muscles are fatigued and you can't do another repetition in perfect form. If you pass the 90-second point and feel as though you could keep going, the weights are too light. If you can't complete three repetitions in 90 seconds, the weights are too heavy. Experiment to find the right weight for you.

The following program stimulates all muscle groups. Do three to six repetitions of each exercise. For exercises that require switching arms or legs, do three to six repetitions with each arm or leg. You will need adjustable hand and ankle weights. Look for sets that can adjust from one to 20 pounds.

●**Push-ups.** Kneel on a towel with your hands on the floor in front of you, shoulder-width apart. Keep your back straight—don't let it sway or arch.

Take three seconds to lower yourself the first inch and at least seven seconds to lower yourself all the way, until your forehead almost touches the floor. Without resting at the bottom, reverse direction. Don't lock your elbows at the

top. As soon as your arms are almost straight, reverse and go back down. If kneeling push-ups are too easy for you, do regular push-ups, with your toes on the floor.

●**Doorknob squats.** Open a door halfway so that you can grip both knobs. Place a stool or chair about two feet from the edge of the door. Stand an arm's length away from the door. Lightly grasp both knobs for balance, and slowly bend your knees and lower your body as though you were sitting down. Take three seconds to lower yourself the first inch and seven seconds to go all the way down, until your bottom just touches the stool. Then reverse and rise back up. Be careful not to pull yourself up with your arms—use the muscles of your buttocks and thighs.

●**Side-lying leg lifts.** Try this exercise without ankle weights at first. If it's too easy, start with five-pound weights. Lie on your left side with your head propped on your left hand. Bend your left leg slightly so that your right leg rests on top of the calf. Slowly raise your right leg toward the ceiling, moving from the hip. Take three seconds to move it the first inch and seven seconds to raise it all the way. Pause at the top, tightly squeezing the hip and buttock muscles for a few seconds. Then slowly lower the leg back down. Repeat with the other leg.

●**Single-leg curls.** Attach a five-pound weight to your right ankle. The weight will probably be too light, but it's a good place to start. Lean forward and put both hands on a stool or chair...keep your right knee slightly bent and your spine straight.

Curl your right leg so that the heel approaches your bottom. Take three seconds to curl the leg the first inch and seven seconds to curl it the rest of the way. Pause at the top, squeezing the muscles in the back of your thigh. Then slowly reverse direction. Repeat with the other leg.

●**Side shoulder raise and overhead press.** This movement combines two exercises. Start with five-pound dumbbells. With a dumbbell in each hand, sit on a chair with your back straight and your feet flat on the floor. Slowly raise the weights away from your sides, taking three seconds to move them the first inch and seven seconds to raise them until they're parallel to the floor. Pause at the top for a few seconds; then slowly lower the weights.

Without resting, move on to the next phase of the exercise. With elbows bent, hold the weights at shoulder height, then slowly raise them overhead, taking three seconds to move them the first inch and seven seconds to go all the way up. Pause for a second; then slowly lower the weights until they're back at shoulder height. Don't lock your elbows at the top. Your muscles—not the joints—should support the weights.

●Single-arm back pull-ups. You need a stool or chair and a six- to eight-pound dumbbell. Hold the dumbbell in your right hand… face the stool with your left leg forward…and support yourself with your left hand on the stool. Let your right arm hang down beside the stool.

Slowly pull the dumbbell back and upward, taking three seconds to move it the first inch and seven seconds to raise it all the way. Your right elbow will be facing up and behind you. Pause at the top, squeezing the arm and back muscles for several seconds. Then lower the weight back down. Don't let your arm hang down at the end of the movement. Keep tension on the muscles all the time. Repeat with the other arm.

●Biceps curls. Sit on a stool or straight-back chair with a five-pound dumbbell in each hand. Tuck your elbows into your sides, and keep them there throughout the exercise. The only thing that should move is your lower arm.

Curl the dumbbells toward your shoulders, taking three seconds to move them the first inch and seven seconds to curl them all the way. Squeeze the muscles in the forearms and upper arms for a few seconds at the top of the movement; then slowly lower the weights back down.

●Shoulder shrugs. Sit on a stool or straight-back chair with a 10-pound dumbbell in each hand. Let your arms hang down away from your hips, with the elbows slightly bent.

Raise the tops of your shoulders as though you're trying to touch them to your earlobes. Sit up very straight. Do not slouch forward or backward. Take three seconds to move your shoulders the first inch and seven seconds to raise them as far as they'll go. Pause at the top to squeeze the muscles in your shoulders; then lower them back down.

●Abdominal crunches. Lie on your back with your feet flat on the floor and your knees bent at a 90° angle. Tuck a rolled towel under your lower back…hold your arms straight in front of you…and keep your chin tucked into your chest. Curl your torso upward and forward, taking three seconds to move the first inch and seven seconds to move forward. Don't try to sit all the way up. Keep your lower back in contact with the towel. Pause and squeeze abdominal muscles at the top of the movement; then slowly lower your torso down. Don't rest your shoulders on the floor at the end. As soon as they brush the floor, repeat the exercise.

Illustrations by Shawn Banner.

How to Beat Osteoporosis

George J. Kessler, DO, clinical instructor of medicine and attending physician, Weill Medical College of Cornell University, and an osteopathic physician in private practice in New York City. He is author of *The Bone Density Diet: Six Weeks to a Strong Body and Mind.* Ballantine.

W ho should be concerned about osteoporosis? The short answer is everyone. Your body builds all the bone density it will ever have by your late 20s. Bone density starts to decline after age 30, and this process accelerates as the body's synthesis of sex hormones slows.

Osteoporosis is especially prevalent among women, although 20% of its victims are men.

Until recently, it was thought that osteoporosis affected mostly Caucasian women, but new evidence suggests that these women are simply more likely to *report* breaks due to osteoporosis. All races are at risk.

NUTRITION AND EXERCISE

Bones *seem* stable as rock. In fact, they're made up of living cells. These are constantly being broken down and replaced by new ones.

Osteoporosis develops when breakdown accelerates and/or rebuilding slows. *But lifestyle strategies can keep the process in balance…*

•**Minerals.** Most of us are well aware that calcium is necessary for bone health. Premenopausal women and men under age 65 need 1,000 milligrams (mg) per day. For postmenopausal women and men over age 65, 1,500 mg is better.

Dairy foods are the classic source of calcium. One cup of milk contains 300 mg, one cup of plain yogurt, 450 mg. But you can also get calcium from beans (100 mg to 200 mg per cup)…kale (90 mg per cup)…and collard greens (350 mg per cup).

Calcium-fortified orange juice contains 300 mg per cup, fortified grapefruit juice, 280 mg per cup. Fortified breakfast cereals typically contain 250 mg per serving.

Soy milk, tofu and other soy products contain not only calcium but also *phytoestrogens* and other nutrients. These natural plant estrogens promote growth of new bone tissue and slow bone loss.

Bones need other minerals, too—notably magnesium and phosphorus—as well as vitamin D. Fortunately, plant sources of calcium also contain the other minerals. You can get all the vitamin D you need from 32 ounces of fortified milk…or from just 20 minutes of sunlight a day. (Skin makes vitamin D upon exposure to sunlight.)

•**Exercise.** The physical stresses to which bones are subjected during exercise stimulate new bone growth. Get at least 30 minutes of walking, weight lifting or another weight-bearing exercise, three times a week.

BONE ROBBERS

To slow the excretion of calcium from your body, it's essential to cut back on certain foods and activities. *Keep an eye on…*

•**Protein.** Each ounce of animal protein you eat causes elimination of roughly 25 mg of calcium. Most Americans get far more protein than they need.

•**Alcohol.** Have no more than three drinks per week.

•**Cigarettes.** Smoking doubles your risk for osteoporosis-related hip fracture.

•**Salt.** An eight-ounce serving of canned soup contains up to 3,000 mg of sodium chloride. Every 500 mg of sodium leaches 10 mg of calcium from your bones.

•**Caffeine.** Each cup of coffee pulls out 40 mg of calcium.

•**Soft drinks.** Phosphorus in sodas promotes calcium excretion.

DO YOUR BONES NEED HELP?

Bone densitometry is a 15-minute outpatient procedure that gauges bone strength. Most women should have the test at menopause—men, at ages 55 to 60. If it indicates a problem, doctors use one of the cross-linked collagen tests—N-Telopeptide (NTx) or deoxypyridinoline (Dpd)—to measure the rate of bone loss. Your doctor will use information from both tests to determine whether you need treatment for osteoporosis.

Depending on the degree of bone thinning, the rate of bone breakdown, your age, gender and other issues, your treatment may include hormones, bone-building drugs and/or medication for an underlying condition (such as an overactive thyroid).

HOW ABOUT HORMONES?

Although hormone-replacement therapy (HRT) may be effective against osteoporosis, for many women the risks of breast cancer, heart disease and stroke often outweigh the benefits.

Whether or not to go on HRT is a personal decision. A woman with a family history of heart disease or breast cancer may want to avoid it. Women should take HRT only if benefits outweigh risks.

Three alternatives to HRT…

•**Estriol.** This weak natural estrogen protects bone without increasing cancer risk. Sold by prescription as a pill or cream, it is not widely available. You may have to ask your doctor to find it for you. If he/she can't help, ask your pharmacist.

•**Natural progesterone.** Another bone-building hormone that declines at menopause or before, progesterone is less likely than estrogen to cause breast cysts, uterine fibroids and insomnia. It's sold over the counter.

•**Raloxifene (Evista).** This prescription drug and other *selective estrogen receptor modulators* are similar to estrogen. They have a real but smaller effect on bone density—and none of the cancer risk. In fact, they can *lower* your risk for breast cancer.

HORMONE ALTERNATIVES

For people who want to avoid hormones, four drugs are worth asking a doctor about…

•**Alendronate (Fosamax).** Available by prescription, alendronate is the drug of choice for men and for bone loss linked to steroid drugs. It slows bone loss.

•**Risedronate (Actonel).** This prescription drug is similar to alendronate but is less likely to cause digestive problems.

•**Calcitonin (Miacalcin).** This prescription drug is often the best choice for people who cannot tolerate alendronate or who prefer a natural rather than a synthetic product. It slows bone loss and decreases bone pain.

•**Ipriflavone.** This over-the-counter derivative of soy protein resembles estrogen. It can be used by women and men and is the only drug that slows bone loss and builds new bone.

Prescription Drugs From Canada

Gary Passmore, spokesperson, Congress of California Seniors, a nonprofit senior advocacy group based in Sacramento with approximately 500,000 members. The group has joined with other senior and health-care advocates to lobby for the legalization of importing prescription drugs from Canada. *www.seniors.org.*

The sky-high cost of prescription drugs in the US has prompted about one million Americans to buy from Canadian pharmacies. Prescription drugs cost less in Canada than in the US because Canada—like most industrialized countries—has price controls to keep down drug prices. America does not have such price controls.

For Americans who have chronic conditions requiring long-term prescriptions that are not covered by insurance, ordering drugs from north of the border can cut the cost of medications by half—and sometimes even more.

Caution: Those with Medicare D prescription drug coverage may find domestic purchases cheaper than Canadian ones.

But is it safe? For answers, we spoke with Gary Passmore, who has toured Canadian pharmacies for the Congress of California Seniors, a senior advocacy group.

•**Why isn't it legal for Americans to order prescription medications from Canada?** According to federal law, the US Food and Drug Administration (FDA) must approve the safety of all pharmaceuticals brought into the country and certify the safety of the companies that handle and sell them. For the past decade, through both the Clinton and Bush administrations, the US government has declined to provide the necessary certification for Canadian pharmacies.

•**Do Americans risk prosecution when they import prescription drugs?** No, not if they do so within reason. While the FDA refuses to take steps to make importing prescription drugs legal, the US Customs Department will not take action against individual Americans who import prescription drugs for their own personal use—if they have valid prescriptions and bring in no more than a 90-day supply. This is according to a statement made before the Senate by William K. Hubbard of the FDA. This applies to drugs sent through the mail or driven across the border. (To avoid problems, bring your prescription with you if you intend to drive.)

•**The US government says that importing Canadian pharmaceuticals poses safety risks. Are Canadian drugs truly less safe than American drugs?** Health Canada (the Canadian department of health) is as rigorous in its inspections of pharmaceutical makers and distributors as the FDA. There has been no documented death or illness caused by an unsafe drug sent to an American from a Canadian pharmacy. The only reason the US government is claiming that there are safety issues is that the pharmaceutical industry has considerable power in Congress and wants Americans to buy drugs at higher prices.

•**How should Americans select a Canadian pharmacy?** I advise sticking with pharmacies that belong to the Canadian International

Pharmacy Association (CIPA). They are listed on CIPA's Web site, *www.ciparx.ca.*

I have met with CIPA's leadership personally, and I'm convinced that it is committed to maintaining high professional standards.

Call the toll-free numbers of a few CIPA pharmacies listed on the site, and use whichever one makes you feel most comfortable. The pharmacist should be able to answer any questions you have about your medications.

•**How much can an American save by ordering drugs from Canada? Is it important to shop around?** The savings vary by drug and with fluctuations in the exchange rate between the US dollar and the Canadian dollar. Generally, you can save between 40% and 80%, even after you account for shipping charges.

Certainly, you should shop around and check the prices at a few different pharmacies—but don't expect prices to vary much because the Canadian government regulates how much pharmaceutical companies can charge.

•**Are prescription drugs exactly the same in Canada as they are in the US?** The medications made for the Canadian market generally are the same as those made for the American market, but occasionally there are minor differences. Some drugs have different names in different countries, and some are different in appearance.

Example: Nexium, a heartburn treatment, is widely advertised as "the purple pill" in the US. In Canada, it's pink.

If you work with a reputable Canadian pharmacy, the pharmacist will explain any differences to you to prevent confusion. Canadian pharmacies are doing a booming business selling to Americans, so they're familiar with the potential sources of confusion.

•**Are Canadian pharmaceutical rules and practices different from those in the US?** Not significantly, but there are two differences worth noting. First, Canadian law requires that the pharmacist receive an original prescription—not a copy—before he/she can provide medication. If you place your order by phone or over the Internet, you'll be asked to mail in your prescription.

Second, Canadian law requires that all prescriptions be approved by a physician licensed in Canada. That isn't a problem for American customers—Canadian pharmacies that deal with international customers have Canadian doctors on staff or on call to provide approvals at no extra fee to the drug buyer. Just be aware that you might receive a call from a Canadian doctor after you order if there is some question about your medical condition or other drugs you're taking.

•**Can any prescription be filled through a Canadian pharmacy?** Most Canadian pharmacies provide only refills for Americans, not initial prescriptions. Side effects are most common when drugs are first used, so responsible pharmacies want a local pharmacy to handle the first order. That way, you have someone nearby to consult if there's a problem.

Most Canadian pharmacies also won't mail insulin or other medications that require refrigeration because they have no way of knowing how long the package might sit on your doorstep. Controlled substances such as morphine usually are not available through the mail either.

•**Should people who live in the American Southwest consider heading to Mexico for their prescription drugs?** I can't endorse that. The Mexican government doesn't have the same level of health safeguards as the US.

•**Is there any chance that the US government will start cracking down on citizens who import their prescription drugs from Canada?** It is unlikely that the US will start arresting people at the border. No politician wants to be seen locking up grandmothers who can't afford to buy their medications at home.

The greater risk to this savings opportunity is that the Canadian pharmaceutical system could be stretched beyond its limit. Some drugmakers now are capping their shipments to Canada so that there won't be enough to fill American orders.

Ordering from Canada is not a long-term solution to our nation's high drug-price problem. The American government is going to have to come up with a better way to make affordable pharmaceuticals available.

•**Can I deduct the cost of drugs from Canada?** No. The IRS has rules that imported prescription drugs cannot be deducted, even though you deduct your other medical costs as an itemized deduction.

Hospital Smarts

Check the quality of care at more than 15,000 US hospitals and other medical facilities. Sponsored by the Joint Commission of Accreditation of Healthcare Organizations. *www.jointcommission.org.*

Hospital Bill Self-Defense

Up to 90% of hospital bills contain errors. Three-quarters of the errors are in the hospital's favor and average about $1,400 per bill.

Self defense: During your hospital stay, keep track of all services as best you can. Ask for an itemized bill each day so that you can track every expense.

Charles B. Inlander, president, People's Medical Society, Box 868, Allentown, PA 18105.

Aspartame Has Side Effects

The popular artificial sweetener aspartame can cause symptoms that are identical to those associated with hyperthyroidism—which is also called Graves' disease.

Symptoms: Heart palpitations, anxiety attacks, headaches, hypertension, hair loss, enlarged eyes.

The symptoms appear most often in people who are dieting and on vigorous exercise programs.

Nan Kathryn Fuchs, PhD, nutrition editor, *Women's Health Letter.*

Lower Stress in 5 Minutes or Less

Dawn Groves, Bellingham, WA–based author of *Stress Reduction for Busy People.* New World Library.

No time to relax? Don't be so sure. *It can take five minutes or less to unwind and refresh your mind…*

•**Move around.** Take a quick trip through the halls of your workplace—or around the block. Walk up and down a flight of stairs. Do 15 jumping jacks.

•**Stretch while seated.** Lace your fingers under your knee, and draw it to your chest. Repeat with the other knee. This stretches the leg and lower back.

Next, stretch your arms above your head, palms up and fingers interlaced.

Drop your hands to your sides, then raise your right shoulder to your right ear, keeping your head vertical. Repeat with the left shoulder.

Finally, bend back the fingers of each hand. This is especially important if you use a computer for long periods.

•**Take 10 long, deep breaths.** Your belly should expand as you inhale and contract as you exhale.

•**Massage your eyes and ears.** Place your palms over your eyes. Slowly spiral your palms while applying gentle pressure. Do the same for your ears.

Blocking out sights and sounds, even for just a few seconds, is psychologically refreshing.

•**Try aromatherapy.** Put a drop of lemon-lime or orange essential oil in a saucer. These gentle scents relax you without making your home or office smell like an incense store.

Great resource: www.aromaweb.com.

You Don't Have to Put Up With Fatigue Anymore

Erika T. Schwartz, MD, an internist in private practice in Armonk, NY. She is author of *Natural Energy: From Tired to Terrific in 10 Days.* Putnam.

You've tried getting more sleep. You've tried exercising and taking other steps to control psychological stress. Yet you're still feeling tired and run down. You know it's unwise to prop yourself up with caffeine. But what else can you do to boost your energy levels?

Once anemia, heart disease, thyroid disease, hepatitis, mononucleosis and other medical causes of fatigue have been ruled out, the average physician is at a loss as to what to do next.

"You'll just have to learn to live with it," he/she might say. Or, "Well, you *are* getting older."

Not true. *These nutrition-based strategies can be very effective...*

DRINK MORE WATER

Many cases of fatigue can be traced to the *mitochondria*, the microscopic "power plants" inside each cell of the body.

Mitochondria synthesize *adenosine triphosphate* (ATP), a high-energy molecule that's used throughout the body as a source of energy. But the chemical reactions that yield ATP also make free radicals and other toxins as by-products.

To flush out these toxins, the body needs at least 64 ounces of water a day. Less than that, and mitochondria are apt to become "clogged" with toxins, becoming inefficient at pumping out ATP.

RECONSIDER SALT

For many people with high blood pressure, salt deserves its status as a dietary no-no. But in healthy individuals, moderate salt intake boosts energy levels.

Salt helps the body hold on to the water it takes in. By boosting water retention, salt helps keep mitochondria free of toxins and functioning properly.

As long as your blood pressure is normal, it's safe to boost your intake of chicken stock, miso soup, salted nuts and other unprocessed sources of salt whenever you feel fatigued.

EAT SMALL, EAT OFTEN

Eating three big meals a day puts your blood sugar (glucose) levels on a roller-coaster. Low glucose can cause fatigue.

Eating every three hours helps keep your energy up by steadying your glucose levels.

Your goal should be to consume a mix of protein and fiber at each meal. Because fiber- and protein-rich foods are digested slowly, they provide a steady, reliable source of energy.

Eat plenty of vegetables, brown rice, multigrain bread, grilled chicken or fish, nuts and dried fruits.

ENERGY-BOOSTING SUPPLEMENTS

Three nutrients are of proven value in the treatment of chronic fatigue...

•**L-carnitine.** This amino acid helps transport fatty acids into mitochondria, where they're used to make ATP.

L-carnitine is found in lamb, beef and other meats, but you would have to consume impossibly large amounts of these natural food sources to get the 1,000 mg of L-carnitine needed each day to boost your energy.

Ask your doctor about taking the prescription L-carnitine supplement *Carnitor*. The typical dosage is three or four 330-mg tablets a day.

•**Coenzyme Q10.** This antioxidant enzyme acts as a catalyst to "spark" synthesis of ATP.

Organ meats are the best source of this enzyme, but you would have to eat far too much to get the recommended 100 mg of coenzyme Q10 per day.

Coenzyme Q10 is sold over the counter in powder or gel form. The gel is more easily absorbed. The typical dosage is two 50-mg gelcaps a day.

•**Magnesium.** This mineral is needed for ATP synthesis. Unfortunately, chocolate, caffeine, soft drinks and highly processed foods tend to deplete the body of magnesium. As a result, magnesium deficiency is common in the US, and fatigue is a symptom of magnesium deficiency.

At special risk: Diabetics, people who consume lots of caffeine and people who take diuretic drugs.

Good sources of magnesium include wheat bran...brown rice...spinach...kale...chicken...turkey...pork...apricots...and curry powder.

Ask your doctor about taking a magnesium supplement, too.

How to Get a Good Night's Sleep

James B. Maas, PhD, professor of psychology at Cornell University, Ithaca, NY. He is author of *Power Sleep*. Villard.

If you're having trouble sleeping, you are probably well acquainted with the basic recommendations for sound sleep...

•**Avoid caffeine and alcohol too close to bedtime.**

•**Avoid nicotine.** If you smoke, quit.

•**Take a warm bath or shower just before turning in.**

•**Get regular exercise and eat a wholesome diet.**

•**Avoid sources of stress late in the evening.**

If insomnia persists despite your best efforts to follow these strategies, the culprit could be your bedroom. *Here's how to set up your "sleep environment" for a restful night of sleep...*

•**Make sure your home is secure.** You will sleep better knowing that your family is protected against fires, burglary and other threats.

In addition to smoke detectors and good locks, consider investing in a burglar alarm.

•**Choose bedroom decor carefully.** Sky blue, forest green and other "colors of nature" are especially conducive to sleep. So are paintings of landscapes...or family photos taken on a favorite trip.

Bedroom office trap: Looking at stacks of bills or other paperwork makes it hard to fall asleep. If your home lacks a den or study, find a hallway or another place in your home to set up your office.

•**Eliminate light "pollution."** The easiest way to keep light from disturbing your sleep is to wear light-blocking eyeshades. You can pick up a pair at a drugstore.

If you find eyeshades uncomfortable, rid your bedroom of illuminated clocks, night-lights and other sources of light.

If streetlamps or other light sources shine in through your bedroom windows, fit your windows with light-blocking "blackout" curtains.

•**Silence environmental noise.** Any sound louder than 70 decibels (the equivalent of a dripping faucet) is disruptive to sleep. *If you cannot eliminate a particular sound, block it using these strategies...*

•Furnish your bedroom with heavy drapes and thick carpeting. If you're building a new home, make sure walls and ceilings have good sound insulation.

•Wear sound-blocking earplugs. Several types are available at drugstores. They cost only a dollar or two a pair.

•Use a "white noise" generator. White noise is high-frequency sound like that produced by rainfall, surf, rustling leaves, etc. It masks other, more intrusive sounds...and helps lull you to sleep.

Low-cost white-noise generator: A bedside FM radio tuned between stations to static. Alternatively, you can play compact discs containing recorded nature sounds...or use an electronic sound-masking device like those sold by The Sharper Image and other retailers.

•**Keep your bedroom cool.** An overheated bedroom can set off the body's wake-up call in the middle of the night. It can trigger nightmares, too.

Best temperature: 65° Fahrenheit.

•**Maintain ideal humidity.** Most people sleep best when relative humidity stays between 60% and 70%. Check it occasionally using a humidity indicator. This simple gauge is available at hardware stores for about $5.

If humidity regularly falls outside this range, a humidifier or dehumidifier can help. These devices are sold at department and hardware stores. They cost from $50 to $200.

•**Buy the best mattress you can afford.** If you like innerspring mattresses, spring count is crucial. A mattress for a full-size bed should have more than 300 coils...a queen, more than 375...a king, more than 450.

If you prefer the feel of a foam mattress, make sure the foam density is at least two pounds per cubic foot.

Whatever kind of mattress you pick, be sure to "test-drive" it at the store. You and your partner should have at least six extra inches of leg room.

Mattress maintenance: Once a month, rotate the mattress so that the head becomes the foot. Flip the mattress, too.

For more information on mattresses, contact the Better Sleep Council, 501 Wythe St., Alexandria, Virginia 22314. *www.bettersleep.org.*

•**Pick good sheets and bedclothes.** If you wear pajamas or a nightgown to bed, be sure the garment is soft to the touch—and roomy. Cotton and silk are more comfortable than synthetics.

When purchasing sheets, opt for cotton, silk or—best of all—linen. It feels smooth against the skin and absorbs moisture better than other fabrics.

•**Avoid overly soft pillows.** People often pick pillows that are too soft to provide proper support for the head and neck.

Down makes the best pillow filling. If you're allergic to down, polyester microfiber is a good second choice.

Some people troubled by insomnia find that a pillow filled with buckwheat hulls is particularly comfortable. These pillows are sold in department stores.

•**Don't be a clock-watcher.** The last thing you want during the wee hours is a visible reminder of how much sleep you're losing.

If you wake up in the middle of the night, don't even glance at the clock. If necessary, get rid of the clock…or turn it to face away from you before you turn in for the night.

•**Keep a writing pad on your nightstand.** To avoid ruminating on fears or "to do" lists as you try to fall asleep, jot them down as soon as they arise. Vow to deal with any problems or obligations the following day.

If worries keep you awake anyway, read or watch television until you feel drowsy.

New Way to Relieve Allergy Misery

A technique called *laser submucosal resection* permanently relieves nasal congestion in patients who haven't been helped by drugs and/or allergy shots.

The 15-minute treatment, often covered by insurance, decreases the size of *turbinates*, nasal structures that swell during an allergic reaction.

Result: Less congestion and allergy-related snoring and fewer sinus infections.

Information: American Academy of Otolaryngology—Head and Neck Surgery, 703-836-4444, *www.entnet.org.*

Rajiv Pandit, MD, an otolaryngologist at Methodist Dallas Medical Center and Dallas ENT & Allergy Center.

Secrets of Youthful-Looking Skin

Nicholas V. Perricone, MD, adjunct professor of medicine at Michigan State University's College of Human Medicine, East Lansing. He is author of *The Wrinkle Cure: Unlock the Power of Cosmeceuticals for Supple, Youthful Skin.* Rodale. For more on skin care, see Perricone's Web site at *www.nvperriconemd.com.*

I n their quest to keep a youthful appearance, growing numbers of men and women are using costly—but ineffective—wrinkle creams and undergoing painful procedures like face-lifts and dermabrasion.

There is an effective alternative. It's not a quick fix, but a science-based change in the way you eat and live.

OXIDATION AND INFLAMMATION

What we call "aging" of the skin—wrinkles, age spots, etc.—is *not* the fault of time. It's the result of inflammation. In fact, you might say that aging is inflammation…and that if you want to attack the first, you must defend against the second.

Inflammation is usually thought of as something obvious—the redness of sunburn, for instance, or painful swelling associated with infection. Actually, inflammation goes on invisibly—and constantly—at the cellular level.

Oxidation is a cause of underlying inflammation. You may have heard that this cell-damaging process is caused by highly reactive molecular fragments known as free radicals.

Ultraviolet radiation from sunlight creates free radicals in the skin. So does air pollution. And so do the natural metabolic processes that the body uses to convert food into energy.

The key to stopping or reversing "aging" is to minimize oxidation—and inflammation.

ANTI-INFLAMMATORY DIET

•**Cut back on sugar.** It's responsible for 50% of skin aging. Sugar molecules react with *collagen*, the protein that gives texture to the skin. That makes skin saggy instead of resilient. And each time sugar reacts with collagen, it releases a burst of free radicals.

In addition to cake, candy and other sweets, it's best to avoid pasta, potatoes, white rice, fruit juices, grapes and cooked carrots. These foods have a high glycemic index—meaning that they are converted into blood sugar very rapidly.

Most fresh fruits and vegetables like broccoli, eggplant, tomatoes and greens are okay because they are absorbed slowly.

CONFIDENTIAL REPORT #3:

The Bottom Line
Guide to
Practically Everything

The Bottom Line
Guide to
Practically Everything

How the War on Terror Is Invading Your Privacy

Identity theft is a serious crime that can make victims feel as if there is no way to keep personal information *private*. To make matters worse, new privacy concerns are arising from the war on terrorism.

Strong antiterrorism laws—along with credit card, discount card, telephone and E-ZPass databases—are allowing the government to monitor what you buy…where and what you eat…what you read…where you travel…and more.

In the name of national security, Washington is scouring databases around the country. It can—and is—monitoring E-mail of specific people and checking some general traffic as well.

However, the government refuses to give details about its surveillance techniques.

Meanwhile, large corporations continue to collect, buy and sell a trove of personal data. These intrusions are cause for worry even if you have nothing to hide.

GOVERNMENT INTRUSIONS

The USA Patriot Act, passed shortly after September 11, 2001, permitted broader government monitoring of every American's activities.

Investigators at the Department of Homeland Security have much greater access to our financial information and credit reports. The Department of Justice used to need a judge's order for every phone it wiretapped. Now, it can apply for a roving wiretap that allows listening in on your phone conversations just because a suspect in an investigation lives or works near you.

Helpful: Modern wiretapping devices emit no sound. Call your local phone company if you think your phone is tapped. It will inspect for listening devices free of charge and alert you to an illegal wiretap. However, it will not tell you about a legal tap.

It remains to be seen whether any of these new government powers can foil terrorism, but

John Featherman, personal privacy consultant and president, Featherman.com, a Philadelphia firm that advises corporations on privacy needs, policies and data protection. He also lectures around the country on identity theft and security.

it is clear that data collectors will know increasingly more about you.

The Pentagon's Total Information Awareness (TIA) system has been charged with mining thousands of government and commercial databases, looking for suspicious patterns in credit card and bank data…medical records…telephone bills…prescription drug purchases…divorce records…and items ordered via mail or on the Web. If you have visited an Arab country or go to Middle Eastern restaurants, your information already might be tracked.

It's hard to gauge just how complete the highly secretive TIA system currently is or what the criteria are for all this data mining. The system is supposed to be fully operational by 2007.

The public-interest Electronic Privacy Information Center (*www.epic.org*) monitors news about the TIA system and how it could affect you. It also offers a page of the best tools for remaining anonymous on the Internet.

Self-defense: It is much harder to be tracked if you use multiple Internet and *free* E-mail accounts, which don't require billing information. You can get free E-mail accounts through HotMail, Excite and other providers.

COMMERCIAL INTRUSIONS

Private companies also are collecting your personal data. Why be concerned? Because the information in many databases can hurt you. In addition, many of the entries in databases are wrong. Even if the information is correct, it's easy to draw the wrong conclusions from data. *Examples of information collected…*

Case #1: Supermarket and pharmacy loyalty cards earn you discounts. But your buying records are beginning to be sold to life and health insurance companies, which use them to evaluate your rates based on your food choices and nonprescription purchases. You might regularly buy something for a friend or relative, but the database logs you as the end user.

Self-defense: Avoid giving your full name when you sign up for "loyalty clubs." See if you can use just a first or last name. Many stores, including Safeway, let you sign up anonymously as "Store Customer."

Case #2: E-ZPass technology was created to speed traffic flow and decrease congestion at highway, bridge and tunnel tollbooths. Several states now use it to issue speeding tickets if you travel too quickly between tolls on a highway. Moreover, E-ZPass records have been turned over to law enforcement to track people and have been subpoenaed in civil lawsuits, including divorces.

Self-defense: Use your E-ZPass selectively— remove it periodically and use cash at tollbooths. Or carry multiple E-ZPasses.

HOW TO CONTROL INFORMATION

Almost 70% of consumers complain that they've lost all control over how their personal information is collected and used by companies.*

Not every piece of data can be protected or is worth expending the energy to protect. Choose your battles. Decide what's most sensitive and when convenience or contributing to the collective security of the country makes sense.

Here are steps you can take to regain some control…

●**Pay cash for purchases you want to keep confidential.**

●**Use a temporary credit card number.** To help reduce fraud, some companies offer free single-use numbers to account holders.

How it works: Use an online service, like the one available from MBNA ShopSafe (*www. mbnanetaccess.com*), to generate a disposable account confidentially linked to your real account. It will allow you to limit how much money an online merchant is able to get and the length of time the funds are available.

●**Keep your Social Security number (SSN) out of circulation as much as possible.** It has become the key piece of ID that unlocks access to your personal data, such as medical, insurance and driver's license records.

Self-defense: Avoid writing your SSN on checks or credit card receipts. Use an alternate ID number, either random numbers you select or the last four digits of your SSN. Tell the customer representative, "I'm concerned about my privacy, so I'd rather keep that information to myself."

*According to a recent Harris poll.

Legally, you can refuse to use your SSN on any transaction other than those with tax consequences—such as getting a job or opening a bank account. For more information, contact Computer Professionals for Social Responsibility, *www.cpsr.org.*

•**Never confirm or provide personal information unless you called the company.** One of the most popular identity-theft scams is account "spoofing."

How it works: You get a call or an E-mail claiming to be from a major company wanting to update your security or billing information. You are directed to a Web site that looks just like that company's billing page, with blank boxes for your credit card number, SSN, etc.

The caller or E-mailer actually is a con artist who will use your personal information to open credit card accounts in your name and charge them to the limit. You won't be responsible for these charges, but straightening out the problem with all the credit card companies and credit-reporting bureaus will take huge amounts of time and trouble.

•**Maintain your Internet privacy.** Downloaded material that you thought you had deleted from your computer still remains on your hard drive. It can be accessed with widely available software.

Self-defense: Free computer programs that permanently erase files are available from *www. pcworld.com/downloads.* Search for "utilities to permanently erase files."

PREVENTING INTRUSIONS AT HOME

•**Stop receiving unsolicited credit card offers by mail.** It will reduce junk mail and make identity theft harder for those who steal from your mailbox.

Self-defense: Contact the credit-reporting industry at the National Opt-Out Center, 888-567-8688, *www.optoutprescreen.com.* Specify that you wish to be *permanently* removed from preapproved credit card offer lists.

•**Stop telemarketers from calling your home** using mass-marketing lists filled with your personal information.

Self-defense: Use the new federal "Do Not Call" registry. It will eliminate most telemarketing calls and provide stronger protection than most state registries.

If you don't block solicitors from calling, the registry requires them to exhibit their phone numbers on your Caller ID. Telemarketers who disregard the Federal Trade Commission (FTC) registry can be fined up to $11,000 for each call to a prohibited number.

Information: National Do Not Call Registry, 888-382-1222 or *www.donotcall.gov.*

Police Impersonator Self-Defense

The color of the flashing lights atop police cars are not standardized across the United States. While red flashers are common, many police forces use combinations on their vehicles, such as blue-and-red and blue-and-white. Other police forces use just blue lights.

Self-defense: To protect yourself from criminals impersonating highway police—without violating the law—turn on emergency flashers when an unmarked vehicle signals you from behind...stay on the road...slow down...then stop at the first well-lighted, populated area, such as a gas station.

Phil Lynn, manager, National Law Enforcement Policy Center, International Association of Chiefs of Police, Alexandria, VA.

How to Avoid Identity Theft

Frank W. Abagnale, president, Abagnale and Associates, secure-technology consultants, Box 701290, Tulsa, OK 74170, and author of *The Art of the Steal.* Broadway Books. Mr. Abagnale's early life was the inspiration for the movie *Catch Me If You Can.*

Identity theft is the fastest-growing crime in the US. The Federal Trade Commission (FTC) estimates that more than 1 million people were victimized last year.

Each victim of identity theft spends months or even years and thousands of dollars trying to clear his/her name.

PREVENTION STRATEGIES

How you can steer clear of identity thieves...

•Don't disclose any personal information until you find out how it will be used (including whether it will be shared with others).

•Pay attention to billing cycles so you can follow up with creditors if your bills don't arrive on time. A missing bill could mean that someone has taken over your credit card and changed the billing address to cover his tracks. If your card has expired and you haven't received a replacement, call the card issuer immediately—someone may have obtained your new card.

•Shred every bill and other documents that contain personal or account information. A shredder costs as little as $25.

•Install a lock on your mailbox to prevent someone from stealing your mail to obtain your account and other personal information.

•Remove your name, phone number and address from marketing lists by contacting the Direct Marketing Association (*www.the-dma. org*). This does not remove your name from all lists, but from many of them.

•Reduce the number of preapproved credit card offers you receive by contacting the credit reporting industry at 888-567-8688, *www.optoutprescreen.com.*

•Order a copy of your credit report once a year from each of the three major reporting agencies. Make sure the information is accurate and that the report includes only legitimate transactions.

Contact: Equifax (800-685-1111 or *www.equifax. com*)...Experian (888-397-3742 or *www.experian. com*)...TransUnion (800-916-8800 or *www.trans union.com*).

Note: You are entitled to one free report each year (*www.annualcreditreport.com*). And, if you have been turned down for credit, you can get a free report if requested in writing.

•Consider subscribing to a credit monitoring service that alerts you within 24 hours of any changes to your credit file (for example, an application for a new credit card).

Examples: PrivacyGuard.com (877-202-8828 or *www.privacyguard.com*)...and Identity Fraud, Inc. (866-443-3728 or *www.identityfraud.com*). Costs range from $60 to $130 per year.

•Consider purchasing identity theft insurance—a new type of policy now being offered in some states to help identity theft victims with the expense of restoring their good name and credit.

The insurance covers the cost of fixing credit records, lost wages for time away from work to talk with credit bureaus and investigators, long-distance phone calls, attorney fees and other costs.

Examples: St. Paul Travelers (651-310-7911, *www.stpaultravelers.com*) and Chubb Group of Insurance Cos. (908-903-2000, *www.chubb.com*). Premiums for $15,000 of coverage with a $100 deductible range from $15 to $30 per year.

•Don't carry sensitive information, such as your Social Security number, PIN numbers or passwords, in your wallet or purse.

•Don't give out personal information over the telephone unless you initiated the call.

•Don't put your Social Security or driver's license number on your checks.

•Don't use easily available information, such as your mother's maiden name, your birth date or the last four digits of your Social Security number, as your password for credit/debit cards, phone accounts, etc.

•Don't have new checks sent to your residence. Instead, pick them up at the bank or have them delivered by registered mail so that you'll have to sign for them.

IF YOU'VE BEEN VICTIMIZED

If you find out that someone has been obtaining credit using your name and personal information, do three things immediately...

1. Contact the fraud department of each of the three major credit reporting bureaus. Report that your identity has been stolen. Ask that a "fraud alert" be placed in your file and add a "victims statement" that creditors contact you before opening a new account in your name.

2. Contact the security department of the creditor or financial institution of any fraudulently accessed or opened account. Close the account, and change passwords on any new account. Tell the creditor or institution that this is a case of ID theft.

3. File a report with your local police or where the identity theft took place. Request a copy of the police report in case the bank, credit card company or other creditor needs proof of the crime later on.

After these initial actions, there are things you should do to prevent additional injury as well as correct any adverse actions to date…

•**Cancel all current checking and savings accounts and open new ones.** See that the bank pays only outstanding checks that you've written and that it doesn't honor checks written by someone else. Contact the major check verification companies to alert them of the theft of your checks. They include Global Payments (800-638-4600, ext. 850), ChexSystems (800-428-9623), Fidelity (800-215-6280), SCAN (800-262-7771) and TeleCheck (800-710-9898).

•**Get new ATM cards,** and use a new PIN.

•**Contact an attorney** if credit bureaus are unresponsive or if the title to your property has been changed. Ask him to send a letter to the credit bureau or county clerk of record.

•**Report the crime to the FTC** by calling its Identity Theft Hotline (877-438-4338) or logging on to *www.consumer.gov/idtheft.*

Important: If you are disputing fraudulent debts and accounts opened by an identity thief, the ID Theft Affidavit issued by the FTC now simplifies the process of cleaning up your credit history. Instead of completing multiple forms, you can use this affidavit to alert companies and the credit bureaus when a new account has been opened in your name. Download the affidavit from *www. consumer.gov/idtheft.*

Safeguard Your Home Against Hidden Health Hazards

Alfred Moffit, senior project manager, Environmental Waste Management Associates, LLC, a full-service environmental consulting company that tests soil, air and water quality, Parsippany, NJ.

Buy a home that has hidden health hazards and you could lose your life savings to a massively expensive cleanup. Ignore the problem and you might be the target of a lawsuit by a neighbor or the home's next owner.

Also, as time passes and environmental regulations tighten, problems may become even more expensive to fix.

Here are five major environmental risks and what to do about them…

UNDERGROUND OIL TANKS

Buried fuel tanks often leak as they disintegrate. Tank removal can cost $1,200 to $2,000, depending on the size and where the tank is located. Fixing a significant leak that impacts soil and ground water can cost $50,000 or more. If neighbors test their well water and discover that it is contaminated because of your leak or there are oil vapors in their home, you can be sued.

The only clue that a tank is leaking is a dramatic, unexplained increase in your heating bills or a heating failure due to water entering the system.

Helpful: Some homeowner's insurance policies cover cleanup costs. Some insurers and tank-installation companies sell tank insurance. Or check with your state's department of environmental protection—it might have programs that help pay for cleanups.

Example: New Jersey has a "Petroleum Underground Storage Tank (UST) Remediation, Upgrade and Closure Fund."

•**Home sellers.** To expedite a sale, present contractor certification from your town that proves your tank has passed a pressure test to detect leaks…or the permit documentation that a former owner removed or properly buried a tank and filled it with sand.

•**Home buyers.** The purchase should be contingent on removal of a buried oil tank or passing of a pressure test.

Cost for a pressure test: $400 to $500.

ASBESTOS

Homes built before 1980 may have asbestos fibers in floor tiles, pipe insulation, roof material, sheetrock—even caulking. Asbestos can cause potentially lethal lung diseases, including asbestosis, mesothelioma and lung cancer. Professional removal costs up to several thousand dollars, depending on the amount of asbestos present.

You might not need to act. As long as asbestos-containing tile or insulation is intact, there's no immediate health risk. If items containing asbestos begin to deteriorate and must be removed, hire a licensed asbestos abatement contractor.

•**Home sellers.** Disclose to potential buyers that you have removed asbestos and whether any asbestos remains.

•**Home buyers.** If the home was built before 1980, make sure the deal is contingent on an asbestos test.

Cost: About $750.

LEAD PAINT

Homes built before 1978 usually have lead paint on walls, doors, trim and window frames. Lead in paint chips or dust can cause developmental problems in children. In adults, it can cause anemia, kidney damage, sterility and damage to the central nervous system.

If lead paint is in good condition, it usually is sufficient to paint over it.

Caution: Repainting is less effective on edges of doors and windows. It might be necessary to remove lead paint from these high-wear areas. Sanding kicks up a huge amount of lead dust, so it's best to hire licensed lead abatement professionals if paint is flaking throughout the home.

Cost: Up to several thousand dollars, depending on the extent of contamination.

•**Home sellers.** You must disclose the presence of lead-based paint in a home built before 1978.

•**Home buyers.** If a seller claims not to know about the existence of lead-based paint, make the deal contingent on a lead paint inspection.

Cost: $400 to $700, depending on the home's size and age.

UNDRINKABLE WATER

Nonpotable well water can dramatically affect quality of life—not to mention a home's resale value. Many water-quality problems can be corrected with a contaminant filter, which costs from a few hundred to several thousand dollars, plus monthly maintenance. If the problem can't be corrected, it might be necessary to drink only bottled water.

•**Home sellers.** Few states require sellers to test well water, but if you know of a problem, you should inform buyers.

•**Home buyers.** Make the purchase contingent on a water-quality test by a reputable environmental firm.

Cost: $350 to $500.

RADON

This naturally occurring radioactive gas is linked to increased risk of lung cancer. Homes sometimes have dangerous levels of this colorless and odorless gas in the basement or on the first floor when there is no basement. The problem can be alleviated with a venting system, but retrofitting one into an existing home can cost up to $10,000, depending on the size of the house and the concentration of radon.

•**Home sellers.** You can present proof that your home has a safe level of radon. However, the buyer probably will perform his/her own inspection. Most mortgage lenders require this test.

•**Home buyers.** A home inspector can test for radon for as little as $50. Do-it-yourself tests are available in home stores, but follow instructions to make sure that the house is "sealed" properly. A reading of more than 4 picocuries per liter of air means that action is required.

The Latest Scams and Rip-Offs: Self-Defense Strategies

Kelly Rote, national spokesperson, Money Management International, a provider of nationwide consumer credit counseling, Houston. *www.moneymanagement.org.*

Dan Brecher, a New York City attorney specializing in claims against brokerage firms.

Matt Brisch, communications specialist, National Association of Insurance Commissioners (NAIC), Kansas City, MO.

Michael Brown, president, CardCops, an online watchdog, Malibu, CA, that helps make selling and shopping online safer. *www.cardcops.com.*

Overzealous debt collectors, phony insurance salespeople and greedy stockbrokers urging customers to put their homes at risk are among the latest rip-offs to watch out for…

"ZOMBIE" DEBT
Kelly Rote
Money Management International

•**Beware of collection agencies trying to collect "zombie" debt**—unpaid consumer bills that creditors already have written off as losses. Debt collectors buy this charged-off debt for just pennies on the dollar and then aggressively squeeze consumers to pay it.

Self-defense: If a collector contacts you about a debt that you don't recognize, don't provide any information. Insist on proof of the debt—the original credit agreement and billing statements.

If you're convinced that you do owe the money and your state's statute of limitations on the debt has not expired, consider settling with the agency for a percentage of the amount owed. State statutes of limitations are listed at *www.creditinfocen ter.com* (click on "Rebuild/ Repair").

Also review your credit reports from Experian (888-397-3742, *www.experian.com*), Equifax (800-685-1111, *www.equifax.com*) and TransUnion (800-916-8800, *www.transunion. com*). If a zombie collector has reported the debt delinquency to the credit bureaus after ignoring your request for proof, it is in violation of the Fair Debt Collection Practices Act. File a complaint with the Federal Trade Commission, and notify each credit bureau.

BROKER MISDEEDS
Dan Brecher

•**More stockbrokers are urging customers to tap home equity to buy securities.** In many cases, they're pitching the chance to borrow at today's relatively low mortgage rates to fund the purchase of high-yielding junk bonds. While junk bonds do sport hefty yields, junk bonds and stocks are risky by nature—and not something you would want to pledge a good chunk of your home against.

Self-defense: Don't refinance your mortgage or use home equity to buy stocks or bonds. If you have done so on the advice of your broker and think the advice was inappropriate, you might have reason to seek restitution.

Reason: Brokers have a fiduciary duty to keep customers' interests and financial strength in mind when recommending investments.

•**Brokerages also are not reporting customer complaints,** regulatory actions and criminal convictions in a timely fashion. They are supposed to inform the National Association of Securities Dealers (NASD) of broker wrongdoings and complaints against them within a month of their occurrence—but this often doesn't happen. This has prompted NASD to censure and fine 29 securities firms for late disclosure.

Investors now will be able to find more up-to-date information on complaints and action against brokers on NASD's Web site, *www.nasd.com.*

Self-defense: If your brokerage has consistently failed to disclose such problems in a timely fashion and you believe that you lost money as a result, you might be able to bring a claim against it. NASD's monthly disciplinary actions are reported in major newspapers and on its Web site.

FAKE INSURANCE
Matt Brisch
NAIC

•**Unlicensed insurance companies**—those that do not have your state insurance department's approval—take your money and issue "policies," but then don't pay when you file a claim. Fake health insurance was sold to more than 200,000 people between 2000 and 2002, according to the most recent data available.

Fake insurance looks attractive because it is less expensive than legitimate policies. The main targets of these fake policies are older adults and small businesses looking to reduce health insurance costs. Scams also are common in life and property/casualty insurance.

Self-defense: Be on the lookout for signs that an insurance policy is fake—high-pressure sales tactics, premiums that are at least 15% lower than those from familiar carriers and/or very liberal coverage rules.

Before you purchase any policy, contact your state insurance department to confirm that the company is licensed in your state. Phone numbers and Web sites for state insurance departments are available from the National Association of Insurance Commissioners at *www.naic.org* (click on "Consumer Information Source"). This site also maintains a database of complaints and financial information about insurers nationwide.

BUSINESS ID THEFT
Michael Brown
CardCops

•**Credit card thieves are ripping off small-business owners** by using a combination of fake Web sites and stolen credit card numbers.

The victims are businesses that *don't* accept credit cards. The crooks pose as the business and set up a bogus Web site. They establish an account in the business's name with a merchant processing provider—also commonly called an independent sales organization (ISO)—which transfers funds between the retailers and the credit card companies. The crooks then use the stolen credit card numbers to ring up "sales."

When the owners of the stolen credit cards see bogus charges on their bills, they complain to the credit card issuers, which reimburse them. The card issuers then demand reimbursement from the real merchants, who actually are the victims.

If your business becomes a target of this version of identity theft, it should not be held liable for phony sales.

Self-defense: Contact the ISO that approved the establishment of the bogus account. It is an ISO's responsibility to verify a merchant's identity, and the ISO should be liable for the charges.

Also: Sign your business up for the *SelfMonitor 2.0* credit-reporting service, available from Dun & Bradstreet (866-472-7362, *www.dnb.com*), which will alert you if a merchant account is opened in the name of your business.

Wise Ways to Protect Yourself from Muggers, Carjackers, Pickpockets, More

Roger Shenkle, president, Survival Solutions, a security consulting firm, Box 476, Gambill, MD 21054. He is a former US Army counterintelligence agent.

There are more than a half million robberies in the US each year—and that figure doesn't include the 150,000 stolen purses and wallets…30,000 carjackings. There are nearly 250,000 rapes, attempted rapes and sexual assaults. These numbers add up to almost 1 million victims. *How to protect yourself…*

MUGGERS AND RAPISTS

Maintaining "situational awareness"—that's military-speak for paying attention to what's going on around you—is the best way to avoid street crime. People get so caught up in their own lives that they don't spot danger until it is too late.

Situational awareness is especially important in places *between* the places where you spend time—the deserted parking lot you traverse to get from the mall to your car…or the empty stairwell you descend to get from your office to the street.

When you leave a building and enter a parking lot or garage, look for lingerers. If you see anyone suspicious, go back and ask someone to walk you to your car. If no one is available, call the police and ask them to send a cruiser. It's usually a mistake to try to rush to your car because there often isn't time to unlock the door, start the engine and drive away.

When you're in a potentially dangerous area, walk with a quick, confident gait. This makes you less appealing to criminals.

Caution: If the choice is between, say, walking confidently through a dangerous-looking group of teens or reversing course—reverse course.

Other high-risk situations…

•**Jogging.** Don't wear headphones unless you are certain your jogging route is safe. Headphones reduce your ability to hear danger. When jogging on a sidewalk, go against the flow of traffic so a vehicle can't follow behind you. On city sidewalks, stay close to the road, not near buildings, to make it harder for a predator to jump you from a doorway. Always avoid secluded areas.

•**ATMs.** After dark or in crime-prone areas, go to an ATM that is located inside a store—not one that is visible from the street. Don't assume that an ATM is safe just because it is in a locked bank vestibule accessible only with an ATM card. Muggers carry stolen cards so that they can buzz themselves in and corner victims.

•**Unfamiliar areas.** If you do not know whether a certain part of town is safe, call the local police department's non-emergency number. They'll tell you what neighborhoods to avoid.

Important: If you're mugged, hand over your money immediately. Try to escape only if your instincts tell you that you might be attacked even if you do turn over your cash. If you decide to flee, try a diversionary tactic. Throw some cash so that the mugger has to choose between pursuing you or retrieving the money. If your assailant tries to force you into a car in a public place, you're usually better off resisting right there rather than being driven to a more deserted site.

CARJACKERS

Most carjackings occur when vehicles are stopped at red lights or stop signs. If you're driving in a neighborhood that makes you uncomfortable, lock your doors and roll up your windows. Turn off the radio to cut down on distractions. When you come to a stop, leave enough room between your car and the one ahead so that you can maneuver quickly. Choose the lane farthest from the curb—you'll have more warning if someone on the sidewalk heads toward your car.

If you think you're about to be carjacked and no other cars are around, run the red light, blast your horn and flash your lights. If a carjacker is beside your vehicle with a gun drawn, let him/her have the car—aside from the engine block, no part of a car is likely to stop a bullet.

If confronted when you're unlocking your car, throw your keys to the side and run so that the pursuer must choose between following you and taking your car.

Carjacking gangs sometimes use a "bump-and-rob" technique—they cause a minor car accident, then steal the victim's car when he/she gets out to exchange insurance information.

Self-defense: If you're involved in a minor accident in a solitary area, stay in your car, keep the engine running and yell through the closed window for the other driver to follow you. Drive to the nearest police station or a well-lit, crowded area—an open gas station is a good option.

If possible, jot down the other vehicle's license plate number and call the police on your cell phone to report the accident and where you're heading.

PICKPOCKETS AND PURSE SNATCHERS

A wallet is best kept in a front pants pocket. If you wrap a thick rubber band around it, you're more likely to feel friction if someone tries to slide it out. A purse should be held firmly against the body, not allowed to dangle freely. A fanny pack should be worn in front, with the zipper closed and secured with a safety pin.

Backpacks are the least secure and should be held against the chest when in high-crime areas.

The most secure spot to keep credit cards, passports or other light valuables is in a flat pouch worn under your shirt attached to a chain or string around your neck.

The most common place to have one's pocket picked is on a train or subway car while it is stopped at a station. The thief takes the wallet and makes a quick escape before the train departs. The victim usually is miles away before he notices his wallet missing.

From the time you board a train or subway until the doors close, keep a hand in the pocket that contains your wallet.

Diversions are another common pickpocket technique.

Example: Someone bumps into you—or stops short in front of you so that you bump into him—while a partner picks your pocket.

Whenever you're jostled, always check for your wallet.

Notorious Ex-Hacker Reveals the Latest Scams

Kevin Mitnick, formerly one of the world's notorious hackers. He spent five years in prison for computer hacking–related charges and began promoting computer security after his release in 2000. He is cofounder of Defensive Thinking, a computer security consulting firm, Las Vegas, *www.mitnicksecurity.com*, and coauthor of *The Art of Deception*. John Wiley & Sons.

A favorite department store calls to confirm your credit card number, or a Web site asks you to select a user name. Both are perfectly common situations—and potential cons.

Every day, high-tech con artists trick some of us into revealing personal account information, computer passwords—even secret corporate files. In 2004, about 10 million Americans fell victim to identity theft. *Here are the latest high-tech cons to watch out for...*

•**Caller-ID con.** Paul receives a call from a credit card company saying that he has been preapproved for a great credit card offer. Paul just assumes the call is legitimate because his phone's caller ID confirms the source, so he provides his date of birth, mother's maiden name, Social Security number and other confidential information.

Problem: Using a widely available telephone switch, a con artist arranged for Paul's caller ID to display the name of the credit card company. The con artist just as easily could have made it Paul's bank, a store he frequents—even the White House. Surprisingly, the ability to post phony caller IDs is an unethical but not illegal use of the technology.

How to protect yourself: Don't trust caller ID. When someone asks for sensitive information, insist on calling him/her back and look up the number.

●**Bogus Web site con.** Susan receives an E-mail at work that includes an attractive offer for a popular piece of merchandise. The E-mail includes a link to a Web page that prompts her to select a user name and password.

Problem: Like many people, Susan uses the same password for all of her on-line accounts. The offer and site turn out to be bogus, but the con artist who sent the E-mail now has Susan's password. With that and her work E-mail address, he can access her company's computers. He also might gain access to Susan's Web-based investment accounts or other password-protected personal data.

How to protect yourself: Use a different password for each Web site and on-line account. Make sure all passwords incorporate letters and numbers. This makes it difficult for hackers to guess them with programs that run through the dictionary. Never keep a list of passwords in an obvious place, and if you use *Windows*, don't let it save your passwords.

Note: The closed padlock image that appears at the bottom of your Web browser when you log on to a Web site means that the site has been certified as secure. This is a good sign that the site administrator has been vigilant about security.

●**Mislaid disk con.** Michael spots a computer disk on the floor of his office's restroom. The label says "Confidential Payroll Data" and carries the company logo.

Problem: Such a "mislaid" disk can be a computer-age Trojan horse left deliberately by a hacker employee or visitor. Once Michael loads the disk on to his computer, the hacker can gain access to his files. Worse, the disk unleashes a virus that crashes the company network.

How to protect yourself: Assume that a "lost" disk was left deliberately. Never put such a disk in your computer. Throw it away, or turn it over to your firm's information services department.

●**Stolen data.** Alan gets a call from his company's payroll department. There has been a computer problem, and his paycheck will be delayed by a week unless he can help replace the lost information.

Naturally, Alan is willing to help. He is asked for his Social Security number, whether he uses direct deposit and, if so, the name of his bank and his account number. This con is especially prevalent at large corporations—hackers realize employees are unlikely to know the names of everyone in the payroll department.

Alan wouldn't give such information to strangers, but the caller knows his name and seems to work for the company. Such information is available from company directories. Hackers can find the directories online or even by digging through the company's trash.

How to protect yourself: If you receive such a call, take the caller's name and say you'll call right back. Then dial your company's switchboard, and ask to be connected to the person in question. Consider it a red flag if the caller won't provide a name and call-back number. If you can't find the caller, notify your office manager so that he can alert everyone at your company.

If you own or manage a business, make it clear to all employees that it is always okay to say *no* to a phone request for confidential information.

Important: Hanging up and calling back might not be enough to stop the most sophisticated con artists. They might be savvy enough with phone systems to have your call rerouted to their phones. For greater certainty, get up from your desk and speak to the caller in person or ask to speak with someone you know in that department.

●**Helpful technician con.** Karen is at her desk when she receives a call from someone in her company's information services department. Would she read him the number on the jack to which her computer is connected? Most large companies label all Internet access ports. Of course, she complies.

Days later, after Karen has forgotten about the first call, someone else calls to see if her Internet connection is working and leaves his number. She soon does have problems and calls back—and gives the man her user name and password.

Problem: Karen's helpful computer technician has just stolen her confidential information. It was he who caused her computer problem by calling her company's information services department and asking for her port to be shut down temporarily for testing. Most information services departments wouldn't question such a request. Once the con artist has Karen's user name and password, he calls the department back and has her port turned back on.

How to protect yourself: When asked to confirm confidential information, ask the caller to read the requested number in his file to you. If he says he doesn't have it handy, say you'll get back to him in a minute with the information. Then call your information services department to make sure you're talking to a real technician. Never let down your guard.

Even if you work from home, this con can be used by someone posing as a technician with your Internet service provider.

Annoying Computer Problems Anyone Can Fix

Raymond Alvin, computer troubleshooter and instructor in New York City. He is author of *The 100 Most Aggravating Computer Problems and How to Get Relief.* Streetbeat.

Some of the most aggravating and common personal-computer problems can be solved easily—even by nongeeks—if you know the steps to take. You can avoid costly repairs by using these strategies to fix the "big six" glitches that plague *Windows*-based computers...*

Glitch 1: Your computer freezes. If your cursor won't move and the computer won't respond to commands, the trouble is mixed

*This advice is for personal computers of recent vintage. Most strategies will work with *Windows 2000* and *XP*, and many also will work with *Windows 98* and 95.

messages. One of your software programs is telling your computer to do one thing...another is telling it to do something else. Unable to resolve the conflict, the computer gets stuck.

Solution: Hold down the "Ctrl" and "Alt" keys and then hit the "Delete" key. If your machine is only partially frozen, the *Windows* security window will open. Click on "Task Manager" to see a report of the status of all programs currently in use. Click on the name of any program listed as "Not responding," then click "End Task." This often resolves the problem, though you're likely to lose any unsaved work within the program.

If "Ctrl-Alt-Delete" fails to get a response—or if your computer freezes again soon after—reboot it by turning off the machine and starting it again.

Restoration: If your computer freezes frequently, perform a "restoration" to revert your machine to the way it was when it was problem-free. Performing a restoration should not cause you to lose recently saved documents or E-mails, but it still is a good idea to back up to an external storage device. You can use a "flash drive" that connects easily to your computer's USB port if you have *Windows 98, 2000* or *XP*...or a Zip or disk backup for an earlier machine. You might have to reinstall any recently installed programs.

In *Windows XP*, click "Start" menu, select "All Programs," then "Accessories." Then select "System Tools" and "System Restore." When the computer asks you how far back you would like to revert, pick a date before the freezing problem began. You usually can go as far back as a few weeks, but this will vary with your computer's storage size and settings.

Alternative: If your computer's freeze-ups began after you installed a particular piece of software or hardware, try removing it and then reinstalling it.

If these steps don't help, check the software or hardware maker's Web site or contact the company for help.

Glitch 2: Your computer is sluggish. When a PC suddenly starts moving noticeably slower and doesn't speed up when restarted, it usually is a sign that there's a virus or worm in the system or the *Windows* system has deteriorated.

Solution: If you haven't already done so, purchase and install antivirus software such as *Norton Antivirus* (*www.symantec.com*) or *McAfee Virus Scan* (*us.mcafee.com*). These programs can identify and remove almost any viruses or worms. Before installing antivirus software, back up your files to an external source.

If this doesn't work: Perform a restoration using the instructions on page 91. Return the computer to a time before it slowed down.

Caution: If your computer began making strange spinning, grinding or ticking noises when it started moving slowly, it could signal a serious problem with the hardware. Your hard drive might need to be replaced.

Best: Back up your files on to an external storage device, and contact a professional immediately. Many electronics stores provide computer-repair services.

Glitch 3: Files won't print. More often than not, the problem is with software, not the printer.

Solution: First check for a problem with the printer itself, such as a paper jam or a depleted ink or toner cartridge. Make sure the wires connecting the printer and the PC are fully secured to the proper ports. If this doesn't help, try reinstalling the printer's "drivers"—the software that tells the printer and computer how to work together. To do this, load the CD or diskette that came with the printer into your computer and follow the instructions to uninstall, then reinstall the driver software.

If you're using the computer and printer together for the first time, check the printer's instruction manual to make sure it is designed to run with your computer's operating system.

If your printer is older than your computer, the printer manual might not have this information. Check the printer manufacturer's Web site for instructions on enabling the printer and operating system to work together.

Make sure the printer is set as your machine's default printer. Select "Printers and Faxes" in your control panel. If a checkmark is next to a different type of printer, right click on the one you want to use and select "Set as default printer."

Glitch 4: A program or file is missing. When a software program, such as *Microsoft Word* or *TurboTax*, seems to have disappeared from your computer, the program itself probably is not missing, just the shortcut icon on the desktop that you clicked to access the program. These shortcut icons are easy to accidentally move or delete.

Solution: To replace a shortcut icon, select "Programs" or "All Programs" in your Start menu. If you see the "missing" program, right click on it and select "Send to" then "Desktop" from the menu that appears. If you can't find any sign of the missing program, check "Add or Remove Programs" in the control panel. If it is not there, you might need to reinstall.

If a file seems to be missing, select "Search" on your Start menu. Click "Documents," then follow the searching instructions.

If the file doesn't appear, perhaps you accidentally deleted it when you backed it up to an external storage device. Return the storage device to your computer, and check it for the missing file.

Glitch 5: Your computer monitor is blank when you start up. If the computer made the usual beeping sounds as it started up, the problem most likely is with your monitor. If your computer doesn't make the usual beeping sounds at startup, the blank screen might mean that your system has crashed. This is a serious problem that usually requires a professional's assistance.

Solution: Make sure all monitor cables and plugs are properly connected. If possible, connect your computer to a different monitor.

If your computer's screen is mostly blank when you start up but displays the message "Non Disk Error," the problem is that a floppy disk or a CD is in your disk drive. Simply remove the disk, and restart your computer.

Glitch 6: Your computer's screen is blue with an error message in white lettering. This is known in the computer industry as the "blue screen of death." It is a sign that your computer has encountered a "fatal exception"—a problem serious enough that it was forced to shut itself down.

Solution: You will have to reboot, but first be sure to jot down the name and number of the error listed in the message on your screen. When you restart your computer, go on-line to Microsoft's product-support Web site (*http://support.microsoft.com*). Search for the error using its name or number. Usually you'll find a document that explains what happened and suggests solutions and ways to avoid future mishaps.

Example: If you get the error message "Bugcheck code 0000008E" while attempting to print a file in *Windows XP*, the site suggests downloading a free "Windows XP service pack" update from Microsoft's Web site, which will allow your computer to avoid this problem in the future.

If Microsoft's Web site doesn't provide any help and the problem happens again, take the machine to a computer-repair shop.

Lesser-Known Uses for Google

You may not know that Google (*www.google. com*), the Internet search engine, can also be used to...

●**Track packages**—enter a FedEx or UPS tracking number.

●**Do calculations**—type in an equation.

●**Convert units of measurement**—for instance, "teaspoons in a gallon."

●**Check on stocks**—search a stock symbol to get the company's share price, plus graphs and financial news.

●**Track airline flights**—type in a flight number for a link to a map of the flight's progress.

Dana Blankenhorn, Internet consultant, a-clue.com, Atlanta.

You Can Stop Those Annoying E-mails

Jason Catlett, PhD, president, Junkbusters Corp., a privacy advocacy group that fights spam, Sterling, NJ. www. junkbusters.com. He testified on the problem before the Federal Trade Commission, the US House of Representatives and the US Senate.

Unsolicited E-mail, or "spam," represents about 65% of all E-mail. The average computer user spends 25 hours a year deleting it.

WHO IS DOING THIS?

Spammers usually are individuals who send out millions of advertisements a day, swamping Internet service providers (ISPs). About 7% of the spam sent results in sales.

Spammers usually work on commission, getting, for example, $50 for each mortgage lead or $85 for each cell-phone sale.

HOW THEY FIND YOU

Legitimate E-mail marketers send E-mails to their customers or rent lists of E-mail addresses. They also allow you to opt out of receiving their mail.

Illegitimate marketers don't adhere to the opt-out rule. They try to prevent anyone from recognizing and blocking their messages. They do this by constantly changing the false return addresses they use and the subject lines on their E-mails.

Some even use software programs to steal E-mail addresses from legitimate chat rooms and newsgroups.

Others legitimately buy address lists from Web sites that collect addresses from visitors.

SPAM DEFENSES

●**Use two E-mail addresses if you receive a lot of spam.** Give your primary E-mail address only to business colleagues, friends and family members.

Use the second address for chatting and shopping online and visiting Web sites that don't have privacy policies. Change this E-mail address when it attracts too much spam.

Free E-mail addresses are available from such sites as *www.yahoo.com* and *www.hotmail.com.*

●**Be careful when signing up for freebies or entering on-line (or off-line) contests** that require personal information. These contests often exist only to collect and sell E-mail addresses. Your chances of winning are minuscule.

●**Decline any requests from your ISP** to list your E-mail address in a member directory.

●**Use a mailbox filter.** Most E-mail applications and services let you block specific E-mail addresses as well as particular words or phrases in the subject line or body of the text, such as "free money" or "X-rated."

In Microsoft *Outlook Express*, for example, click on "Tools," then "Message Rules," then

"Mail." Then you can create rules for the words and addresses that you want blocked.

•**Buy antispam software.** It is more sophisticated than the free tools that are in your E-mail application.

Favorite: McAfee Internet Security Suite 6.0, available at *www.mcafee.com.*

•**Complain.** Forward fraudulent and deceitful spam to the Federal Trade Commission at *uce@ftc.gov.*

WHAT THE GOVERNMENT IS DOING

A federal law to regulate spam went into effect on January 1, 2004, making it illegal for anyone to send unsolicited commercial E-mail using a false return address or misleading subject line…collect addresses off Web sites…or fail to use a mechanism that allows recipients to opt out of getting future mailings. The penalties include fines and jail time.

In August 2004, Attorney General John Ashcroft announced that federal and state law-enforcement agencies had arrested or charged dozens of people with crimes related to junk E-mail, identity theft and other online scams.

Better E-mail Solicitations

Be sure that your E-mail solicitations include postal contact information.

If they don't, your company could face stiff fines under the Controlling the Assault of Non-Solicited Pornography and Marketing Act (CAN-SPAM) of 2003. The Act requires that all unsolicited E-mail include the sender's valid physical postal address. It imposes penalties of up to $25 per E-mail—to a maximum of $1 million.

Be especially careful if you use a third-party E-mail provider—you still may be held liable if that provider fails to include contact information on your E-mails.

Alan Fisch, JD, technology law expert and partner, Howrey Simon Arnold & White, LLP, Washington, DC.

Best Way to E-mail Your Résumé

Don't attach your résumé to an E-mail, unless you are asked to submit it that way. Instead, copy and paste it into the body of your E-mail message.

Reason: Like most firms, employment agencies are reluctant to download documents that might carry computer viruses.

Be sure to correct any type styles that might be lost in the copy-and-paste process, such as boldface or underlined text.

Katie Yeakle, executive director, American Writers & Artists Institute, Delray Beach, FL. *www.awaionline.com.*

Job Interviewers' Sneaky Tricks

Job hunters beware. Questions that seem like friendly small talk during or immediately after a job interview might be part of the screening.

•**If the interviewer notes your previous places of employment** and says, "I can understand why you left. I've heard complaints about the upper management there," don't take the bait.

Be either positive or neutral when asked about your relationship with previous employers, co-workers, neighbors, family or anyone else.

•**If an interviewer asks, "What do you do for fun?"** avoid giving answers that center entirely on you.

Rather than say, "I like to golf and watch baseball on television," say, "I like to golf with good friends and watch baseball games with my children."

The interviewer may be trying to determine if you enjoy socializing. The appropriate answers indicate that you are more likely to work well with others.

John McDorman, managing partner, Transition Consulting, a search and outplacement firm in Dallas.

Over 50 and Out of Work: Beat the Age Barrier

Jean Erickson Walker, EdD, professional effectiveness coach, Pathways/OI Partners, Inc., which specializes in coaching people at midlife, Portland, OR, *www.oipartners. net/pathways*. She is author of *The Age Advantage: Making the Most of Your Midlife Career Transition*. Penguin. For more information, go to *www.theageadvantage.com*.

Finding a new job isn't easy. It can be especially hard for people over age 50 because of age discrimination. Employers tend to believe younger candidates are more familiar with new technology, and they can pay younger employees less.

Discrimination is generally subtle and not always deliberate, but the result is brutal. It takes people over age 50 nearly 40% longer to find new jobs as those under 35.* The Age Discrimination in Employment Act of 1967 is intended to protect most people age 40 and older from discrimination in hiring, layoffs, salary, promotion, assignments and training.

Victims of age discrimination can sue employers or prospective employers—but these cases are difficult to prove. The employer can say that the candidate simply wasn't the best person for the job.

The best strategy is to *outsmart* age discrimination. *Here's how...*

●**Confront technology-skills stereotypes head-on.** When a 25-year-old applies for a job, everyone assumes he/she has computer skills. When a 55-year-old applies, many assume he/she does not.

Self-defense: Mention technological expertise during interviews. On your résumé, list computer programs you know or any special certifications you may have.

Example: Ken, 56, agreed to take early retirement after 27 years at his job. For four years, he searched unsuccessfully for a similar management post. At my suggestion, he got his project management certification. Then he positioned himself as an up-to-date telecommunications manager with extensive experience. Now he has a great new job.

●**Select appropriate companies and industries.** If possible, visit the company to get a sense of its culture. If it doesn't feel like a good

*Study by the human resources consulting firm Drake Beam Morin.

fit, look elsewhere. If you have been laid off from a youth-focused industry, emphasize your transferable skills or, if necessary, leave the industry. The technology, telecommunications and advertising sectors tend to favor younger hires.

The banking, government and utility sectors frequently hire younger employees and promote from within. An older job applicant in these industries should angle for a consultant's role rather than a promotion-track position.

Each year, AARP compiles a list of the top companies for older workers. To see the most recent list, go to *www.aarp.org/money/careers/employer resourcecenter/bestemployers*. Industries with the best opportunities now include teaching, health care and retail.

●**Dress for success.** Match the culture you're hoping to join, but also look sharp. Clothes are only as good as the body wearing them. Get in shape. Managers want to hire people who look like they could run—and win—a race.

●**Show flexibility.** A common stereotype holds that an older worker thinks his way is the only way to do things and that he won't even consider new ideas.

Self-defense: Design a résumé that reflects a range of positions and changing responsibilities. This is especially important if you have worked for the same firm for many years.

Example: Mention occasions when you implemented cutting-edge strategies.

●**Play the role of "possibility thinker" in interviews.** Mention a possible scenario, and run through the company's options should it actually occur. When young people do this, they come off as loose cannons trying to fix things that aren't broken. When older, more experienced people do it, they seem adaptable and innovative.

●**Don't abbreviate your résumé**—contrary to standard advice. Some older applicants include only their most recent experience.

Let your résumé run two or three pages, so long as each description is succinct and demonstrates your accomplishments. Don't try to hide your age by withholding employment dates. Emphasize how your experience can help the firm deal with problems.

For information on your rights...

•**AARP,** 888-687-2277, *www.aarp.org/money/careers.*

•**US Administration on Aging,** 202-619-0724, *www.aoa.gov.*

•**US Equal Employment Opportunity Commission,** 800-669-4000, *www.eeoc.gov.*

Best Places to Retire

Kenneth A. Stern, CFP, founder and CEO, Asset Planning Solutions, San Diego, CA. He is author of *50 Fabulous Places to Retire in America.* Career Press.

If relocation is part of your plan for retirement, don't rush into it. *Before making a decision, consider the "four Cs" that make a place suitable for your particular lifestyle...*

Crime: Is the community safe?

Climate: What kind of weather and seasonal changes do you enjoy? Don't assume that the place you love to visit in summer will be equally agreeable in the winter.

Cost of living: Can you afford to live there? Can you find work/business opportunities there if planning on a post-retirement career?

Culture: Do the local residents share your interests?

Where people are retiring to now...

NORTHWEST

•**Eugene, Oregon.** Located 110 miles from Portland, it's close to the ocean and the mountains. It has a moderate year-round climate and offers a variety of outdoor activities, including world-class skiing, river rafting, hiking and fishing. Local colleges provide great continuing-education programs.

Drawbacks: Occasional air-quality problems ...above-average living costs, including taxes and medical expenses.

•**Medford, Oregon.** Located about 170 miles from Eugene, Medford is a small, laid-back town with plenty of outdoor recreational opportunities, including golfing, skiing, fishing or just enjoying the mountains or picturesque Oregon coast. The world-renowned annual Shakespeare Festival in Ashland runs from mid-February through the end of October.

Other advantages: Below-average living costs...affordable housing...part-time jobs and start-up entrepreneurial business opportunities.

•**Bellingham, Washington.** About halfway between Seattle and Vancouver, it offers outdoor recreation in the nearby Pacific Ocean and Cascade Mountains, including fishing, skiing, kayaking and golf—as well as many trails for jogging and walking while enjoying the spectacular natural beauty of the Pacific Northwest.

This small, relaxed community also offers the cultural amenities of a university town (Western Washington University).

Drawbacks: Very wet—170 rainy days a year...limited job opportunities.

FLORIDA

•**Ocala.** Located in north central Florida, about 40 miles from Gainesville, it's one of the world centers for thoroughbred horse breeding. It offers plenty of outdoor recreational activities without crowds of tourists.

Other advantages: Below-average housing and living costs.

Drawbacks: No public transportation, limited shopping.

•**Kissimmee.** Located in central Florida—18 miles from Orlando, so your grandchildren won't need any urging to come visit you. Apart from nearby Disney World and other attractions, Kissimmee offers boating and fishing on the Chain of Lakes, and lots of wildlife.

Drawback: Floods of tourists.

LAS VEGAS

The self-styled entertainment capital has no income tax, inheritance tax or estate tax. Las Vegas has more than 320 days a year of sun and low humidity, year-round golf and tennis, and nearby state and national parks and skiing, hiking and canoeing. There are also many cultural offerings, along with excellent health care and senior services.

Drawbacks: July and August temperatures often exceed 105°F...heavy traffic...high crime rate.

THE SOUTHWEST

•**Austin, Texas.** The state capital of Texas is a rapidly growing metropolis with year-round outdoor recreation, a rich cultural environment and impressive health-care facilities.

Drawback: Hot summers.

•**Brownsville, Texas.** Located in the Lower Rio Grande Valley in southeast Texas, it has a Mexican heritage and a multicultural lifestyle. The cost of living is well below average. Matamoros, Mexico, with even lower prices, is a much larger city within walking distance.

Other advantages: Superb hunting, fishing and exceptional bird-watching.

Drawbacks: Hot, humid summers…heavy cross-border traffic and a high crime rate—particularly car theft.

•**Las Cruces, New Mexico.** Located on the southern border of the state, it's about 45 miles from El Paso, Texas. Las Cruces is surrounded by fabulous landscapes, including the Organ Mountains, the Chihuahua Desert and the Rio Grande. It offers great entertainment, arts, recreation and cultural attractions, beautiful weather, wonderful shopping and dining—all at affordable prices.

Drawback: Springtime dust storms.

RETIREMENT ABROAD

If you don't mind a major culture change and really want to stretch your retirement dollars, consider moving abroad…

•**Mexico.** Some of the places attracting an increasing number of Americans include Tijuana, comfortably close to San Diego…and Rosarito, about 200 miles down the Pacific coastline. One thousand miles further south is Puerto Vallarta, a charming coastal resort.

•**Costa Rica.** San José, the country's capital, has much to offer, including a climate milder than Florida's, the lowest crime rate of any foreign community that's popular among US expatriates, and friendly people—most of whom speak English.

•**The Bahamas.** Nassau, a tropical paradise, is now an offshore banking haven attracting an increasing number of retirees. You don't need to worry about learning a new language in this English-speaking nation.

Caution: Medicare will not pay benefits if living in a foreign country so consider how you are going to pay for health care.

THE RELOCATION DECISION

Even if a particular community seems ideal on first sight, don't buy until you have spent time there on several occasions—and during different seasons. If it still appeals to you, rent for a year before you buy a new home to make sure you are in the right place.

Avoid Challenges to Your Will

Following are a few things you can do while you are alive to prevent your will from being contested after you're gone…

•**Use a *living trust* to handle the estate.** The longer the trust is in operation, the less likely a challenge will be successful.

•**Videotape the situation surrounding the signing of the will,** to show that you are competent.

Trap: A no-contest clause disinherits anyone who contests the will. But such clauses are invalid in many states and are useless if nothing is bequeathed to the person in the will.

Caution: If anyone is disinherited in the will, the document should explain why. Be sure that the explanation is factually correct.

Example: A child has not been in contact for 10 years.

Stanley Hagendorf, estate and tax attorney in private practice with offices in NY and FL. He is a former professor of law in the estate-planning program at the University of Miami School of Law and author of numerous books on various aspects of estate taxes.

How to Avoid "Buck-Passing"

How do I get the government to respond to complaints about Social Security benefits, housing issues, etc.?

Federal government buck-passing is legendary. *Here are some strategies for finding the right person to help you…*

•**Select "Contact Us" at the particular agency's Web site.** Most now have this feature, which includes names and titles, E-mail and mailing addresses and telephone numbers.

●**Access the US government's official Web portal.** At *www.firstgov.gov*, you can browse an A-to-Z agency index as well as state and local government pages.

●**Contact the Federal Citizen Information Center** (888-878-3256, *www.pueblo.gsa.gov*). This agency provides answers to many consumer questions as well as government contact information. Much of the information also is available free in the *Consumer Action Handbook.*

●**Find out if the agency has a problem resolution office.** Address your complaint there.

Ellen Phillips, owner of Ellen's Poison Pen, consumer advocacy consultant, Alexandria, VA, and author of *Shocked, Appalled, and Dismayed! How to Write Letters of Complaint That Get Results.* Vintage.

Collecting More on Your Company Health Policy

Leonard Stern, president, Leonard B. Stern & Co., an insurance consulting and brokerage firm, 65 E. 55 St., Suite 303, New York City 10022.

Health insurance policies are not etched in stone. There are contractual provisions in the insurance policy that are negotiable.

Most companies give health insurance to engender goodwill with employees.

Many problems in collecting the maximum due you are a result of incompetence or negligence on the part of the administrators in your company who handle insurance benefits. They may be too busy or unaware of how to get more for you.

Three ways to improve your ability to collect…

●**Know the insurance contract and all its provisions.** Be aware that everything is negotiable.

Example: Home health care by someone other than a registered or practical nurse is not covered in the policy. Contractually, nothing needs to be said, but administratively, an alternate source of home health care could be covered. It is really a question of negotiation.

●**Have the company's insurance broker help negotiate with the insurer.** He/she is the one who is making the money from selling your company the policy. He also has more leverage than you do with the insurance company. If he

is unwilling to help, encourage your company to switch to a more cooperative broker.

●**Set up a liaison.** The individual in your company in charge of claims should have a good working relationship with the insurance company.

Reason: If the settlement is too low or doesn't fully cover your needs, the claims person at your firm can make a better settlement. After all, the insurance company is selling the policies.

Strategy: If your claims person is uncertain whether you can get more compensation for an ailment or treatment, ask for permission to contact the broker. The broker should know the terms of your contract and be familiar with the people at the insurance company. He should have an idea of how to get the claim paid, especially if it's a legitimate claim but a trifle unusual.

●**Take advantage of situations in which both you and your spouse are covered** by group insurance policies to increase your benefits.

Example: You both have Blue Cross to cover hospitalization and, in addition, you both have major medical. Typically, the major medical has a $100 deductible. The insurance company will pick up 80% of the next $2,000 and 100% thereafter. However, if you and your spouse coordinate your policies, you could wind up using each other's policy to pay the remaining 20% of the $2,000.

Don't expect to make a profit by having several insurance policies.

Years ago, many health-insurance policies were not coordinated, and it was possible to get duplicate payments. Today all plans are coordinated so you can't get duplicate payments.

Trying to make specifically unallowable treatments allowable: This is between the doctor and you.

For instance, if you want to claim cosmetic surgery necessary for health reasons, consult your doctor. If he won't go along with it, you are not going to get anywhere with the insurance broker, the personnel at your office or the insurance company.

If you are stuck with a flawed company policy and find you have huge deductibles and other uncovered expenses, take out a personal policy that coordinates with the company's.

First Aid for Air Travelers

Air travelers should pack a bottle of baby aspirin in their carry-on baggage. Aspirin isn't always included in the medical kits aboard commercial airliners—even though its clot-busting effect can be lifesaving in case of a heart attack. If you think you're having a heart attack, chew one of the 81-milligram (mg) tablets while seeking emergency medical assistance.

Victor S. Sloan, MD, clinical assistant professor of medicine, University of Medicine and Dentistry of New Jersey, New Brunswick. His suggestion was published in the Annals of Internal Medicine.

Better Hotel Stays

When registering at a hotel, ask for something specific, such as a room with a view or one closer to the elevator, etc. This eliminates the chance that you will get struck with an undesirable room. If you have stayed at the hotel before, mention that when you check in. Never settle for an unacceptable room—instead, call the front desk and ask for a reassignment. If you are planning to stay a week or more, write the hotel manager personally at least one week ahead of time and ask for a "space-available" upgrade, price break or extras such as restaurant credits or free shoe shines. At check-in, ask to meet the manager to say hello.

Chris McGinnis, travel correspondent, CNN Headline News, *Atlanta, and author of* The Unofficial Business Traveler's Pocket Guide. *McGraw-Hill.*

Wrinkle-Free Packing

Book of Everyday Solutions. Bottom Line Books.

If your travel is more than overnight and the occasion calls for multiple dress-up outfits, you will want to pack a single suitcase as efficiently as possible.

According to the authors of *Packing: Bags to Trunks* (Knopf), the tissue or plastic bag method is effective...

•**Place tissue paper or plastic bags between each layer of clothing.** This lets garments slide rather than rub.

•**Interlock belts and run them along the circumference of the suitcase.** Place trousers waistband to waistband with the legs left to hang outside the case. Add a layer of tissue to the surface.

•**Place blouses and shirts facedown folded,** using a long fold to turn up the bottom of the garment a third to avoid a mid-belly crease. Add more tissue.

•**Turn suit jackets inside out.** Roll up ties and tuck them inside jacket pockets. Add another tissue layer.

•**Now the pant legs.** Fold them over the top. Add more tissue. On top of that add sweaters and socks laid out flat, not rolled.

•**Shoes, stuffed with underwear,** go into bags (plastic or fabric) and get stuffed in the sides of the bag along with the toiletry kit.

How to Turn Slot Machine Odds in Your Favor

Dwight Crevelt, slot-machine engineer and president, Crevelt Computer Systems, a consultancy to the gaming industry, Las Vegas. He is coauthor (with his mother, Louise Crevelt) of Slot Machine Mania. *Gollehon Press.*

The odds of winning on slot machines almost invariably favor the casino. However—by using the proper strategies—you can increase your chances of striking it rich with one lucky pull.

Key factor: The machine's payback percentage—the proportion of the money wagered that is returned to the players over the long run. If the payback is 95%, the machine returns $95 for every $100 wagered—with $5 held as casino profit.

If the payback is 85%, the machine would return only $85, with $15 going to the casino. A higher payback percentage will help conserve your stake and make it less likely that you'll "bust" before your casino visit or vacation is over. At the same time, it will allow you more opportunities to hit a big jackpot.

Best place to play: Las Vegas, where the payback runs 92% to 97%.

Next best: Reno, at 92% to 95%.

Least favorable: Atlantic City, at 85% to 92%.

In Las Vegas, the best machines of all can be found at large casinos off the Strip (Las Vegas Boulevard), such as Sam's Town, the Gold Coast and the Santa Fe. These casinos cater less to tourists and more to discerning local players, who will go wherever the odds are most favorable.

100+% payback: In their never-ending game of one-upmanship, several off-the-Strip casinos are now offering slot machines that pay back more than 100%. The longer you play at this type of machine, the more you can expect to win.

The catch: There is no way of telling where these machines are located.

On the other hand, if you find a near-deserted bank of machines in an otherwise busy casino, there's probably a good reason—the players have migrated to where the paybacks are better.

Advice: If you have a choice, play where there are a lot of people and where it's busy.

Wherever they gamble, too many slot players are led astray by popular myths…

Myth No. 1: Play the machine nearest the door or on the aisle. Years ago, casinos might have tried to attract passing tourists by placing their higher-payback percentage machines in high-traffic areas. But the machines have now become so popular that casinos have no need for such tactics.

Fact: The only reason to play a machine on an aisle is for comfort, as you won't be crowded by other players on either side of you.

Myth No. 2: If the machine pays back with hot coins, it's a "hot" machine.

Fact: Coins come out of some machines hotter than others because of their proximity to lights or other electrical components in the machine. Their temperature has nothing to do with the machine's payback percentage.

Myth No. 3: "I've put so much money in it, it has to be ready to hit." Today's slot machines are controlled by microprocessors. These miniature computers generate random outcomes

of winning or losing symbols according to the millisecond that you insert your coin or pull your handle.

There is no such thing as a "pay cycle" or "cold cycle" on these machines. Each play is independent of the next. Since jackpots are produced by timing, rather than any given number of pulls, there is no way to predict when a machine is more likely to "hit."

Let's say you play a machine for an hour and lose $50 before you end your session. As you collect what's left of your stake, another player pulls the handle of "your" machine and hits a four-figure jackpot on his very first try.

Before you start cursing your luck, remember—had you stayed to play, the odds are overwhelming that you wouldn't have won that jackpot. The hit was triggered not by the pull of the handle but by the precise timing of the play.

Myth No. 4: If a machine isn't paying, stop playing the maximum number of coins. Drop down to one coin and increase your bet to the maximum when the machine "warms up" again.

Fact: You should always play the maximum number of coins (generally between two and five), for the simple reason that the top jackpots award a significant bonus for maximum plays. If you play less than the maximum, you'll be donating an extra 2% to 5% advantage to the house.

Strategy: If you just can't afford to play the maximum, drop down to a lower-denomination machine.

Example: It's more advantageous to play four quarters than one quarter on a machine with a $1 maximum.

SMART MONEY STRATEGIES

The most successful slots players are those who are disciplined in their money management…

•**Set a strict gambling "budget" for your trip**—an amount you can afford to lose without any guilt or hardship.

•**Divide your stake by the number of days you plan to play.** If you've budgeted $300 for a three-day weekend, you can risk no more than $100 per day.

•**Set a time limit for each session** (an hour or two is reasonable) and buy a limited number of coins—say, $25 in quarters.

●**Don't play back any coins that drop in the tray.** Use only your original "buy." When those coins run out, take stock of what you have in your tray.

If you're ahead, cash in at the change booth and place your profit in the "winning section" of your purse or wallet. This money is untouchable. If you're behind, add whatever you have left to your original stake.

●**If you're behind, take a break.** If you're ahead, buy more change with another portion of your original stake and play that out. Then proceed as described above.

●**If you've played half your stake and lost most or all of it,** change your game plan. Change to a lesser-denomination machine (quarters instead of dollars, nickels instead of quarters, three-coin instead of five-coin).

●**If you're ahead and your machine keeps you ahead with each cash-in,** keep playing. But once your last cash-in amount is considerably less than the amount of stake spent, it's time to move on to a new machine—if only for psychological reasons.

●**If you've played your allotted time** and still have some of your original session stake, consider yourself lucky. Move what's left to your "winnings" pocket. This money is also untouchable—never bet your winnings!

●**It doesn't pay to play two casino slot machines at the same time.** It is not true that one of two side-by-side machines is sure to be hot. Since the house has an edge in all slot machines, playing two at once is simply, on average, a way to lose more money more quickly.

Also, playing more than one machine makes it harder to keep an eye on personal belongings—increasing the risk of theft.

BOTTOM LINE

If you play on indefinitely for a big jackpot without conserving your smaller wins, the casino's advantage is almost sure to wipe you out.

Even if you eventually hit your jackpot, it's unlikely to outweigh your accumulated losses. You must accept every win, no matter how large, for what it is—a victory against the odds.

Winning Strategies for Texas Hold 'Em

Phil Hellmuth, Jr., nine-time World Series of Poker champion and one of the most respected Texas Hold 'Em tournament players. He is author of *Phil Hellmuth's Texas Hold 'Em* (HarperTorch) and *Play Poker Like the Pros* (Harper-Resource). *www.philhellmuth.com.*

Texas Hold 'Em, the poker game favored by professional poker players, is rapidly becoming the favorite game of amateurs as well.

The rules of Texas Hold 'Em are simple. Each player receives two cards facedown. After a round of betting, three cards are dealt face up for players to share (called the "flop"). There's a second round of betting, a fourth card up (the "turn"), a third round of betting, a final up card (the "river"), then one more round of betting.

Players make their best five-card hands out of their two "pocket" cards and the five "community cards" face up on the table. While the rules are easy to learn, those who know Texas Hold 'Em only from watching TV tournaments often run into trouble when they try to play. *Here, winning strategies...*

●**Start tight.** When you watch poker on TV, the professionals seem to play lots of hands. That's because TV coverage shows only key hands. In most home games, the bets are small, so the best strategy is to play extremely "tight," folding most of the hands you're dealt. Play only when dealt one of the 10 best two-card starting hands—pairs of 7s or higher, or an ace-king or ace-queen. When you do get one of these great starting hands, always raise or reraise—don't just call (match a bet).

Exception: If a very conservative player already has made a big bet in front of you and you have a pair of 7s, 8s or 9s, you should fold.

Playing only strong hands will boost your odds of survival while you learn and perfect your game, and you will earn a reputation for playing only great cards, which will make bluffing easier later on.

●**Raise after the flop even if it didn't help you.** The flop is the first three community cards turned over. Often, they won't be the cards you want—but your opponents may not want them either. Rather than not betting on a disappointing flop, make a bet to find out where you're at. Maybe your opponents will fold or call rather than raise, indicating that you might not be in such bad shape after all. (If a raise and a reraise are made before it's your turn to bet, fold if your hand isn't strong.)

Example: You hold 10-10, and the flop comes king-queen-2. With two cards on the table higher than your 10s, someone might have hit a higher pair, putting you at a big disadvantage—or then again, maybe no one was holding a king or queen. If you don't bet, someone else likely will—and you'll have to assume he/she made his hand and fold. If you do make a small bet and no one raises, it may tell you that you're still ahead and may confuse your opponents.

● **Learn to read your opponents.** Even after you fold, time at the poker table shouldn't be wasted. Pick one or two of your opponents and try to guess what cards they're holding based on their behavior and bets. Watch for patterns. Do they only raise on big hands? Do they act especially confident when they have nothing?

● **"Slow play" the occasional big hand.** Once your opponents get used to you betting big on great hands, throw them a curve. If you have ace-ace or king-king, call before the flop. You might make the other players believe that your hand is weak and win a bigger pot. Even if you don't, you'll make it harder for them to figure out what you have later.

In no-limit or pot-limit Hold 'Em, in which pots can grow large, it might be worth seeing a flop (matching a bet before the flop) with a small pair if you can do so cheaply. The odds of hitting three of a kind still are against you, but if you do hit, you might be able to build a big enough pot to make it worthwhile.

How to Get Out of Embarrassing Situations

Letitia Baldrige, renowned expert on manners who in the early 1960s was Jacqueline Kennedy's White House chief of staff. She is author of several books, including *Letitia Baldrige's New Complete Guide to Executive Manners*. Simon & Schuster.

When you make a mistake in a social setting, it is usually awkward for everyone there. But, the damage can be controlled if you know how to gracefully wriggle out of sticky situations. *How to handle highly embarrassing moments...*

● **Someone gives you a holiday gift—but you don't have one in return.** Be effusive in your thanks, and talk about how thoughtful the gift is. Do not apologize for your lack of a gift. It will only draw attention to the awkwardness of the situation.

As soon as you can, write a thank-you note stressing how surprised you were and how much you are enjoying the gift.

If it is from a business associate, you can refuse it by referring to company policy. However, be gracious.

Important: Don't rush to buy the person a gift. It looks phony, and you'll have to buy that person a gift next year. Give presents only to those close to you.

● **You suddenly must introduce someone whose name you've forgotten.** If it is someone you've just met, an easy way around the problem is to gently touch the person's arm and say, "Forgive me, I didn't catch your name." Avoid saying, "Sorry, I've forgotten your name." It is less embarrassing not to have heard the name than to have forgotten it. If it is a person you've met before, put your hand to your forehead and say, "I'm an absolute idiot. Today, I can't even remember my own name."

Everybody forgets names. The person who gets most upset is the person who forgot the name, not the person whose name has been forgotten.

Key: Get beyond the mistake quickly.

● **You make a remark and realize that you have unintentionally hurt the person with whom you're speaking.** This happens frequently, especially when people feel comfortable enough to express themselves honestly.

Solution: Don't try to undo the remark—just move on to the next topic as quickly as possible. Then, when the person starts to leave the group, go up to him/her and humbly apologize. If you act genuinely upset and your apology is heartfelt, most people are eager to forgive you. In fact, at this point, most will be more concerned about your discomfort than about their own.

Use the same approach when your child makes a disparaging comment about someone's appearance. As you leave the room, whisper to the person, "I hope you can forgive my child."

•**You show up at a dinner party with an uninvited date—only to discover that your role was to be the eligible man or woman.** This is a real gaffe and it is something that usually becomes apparent by your host's immediate discomfort.

Solution: Take your host or hostess aside and whisper your apologies. Don't tell your date about the mix-up. Otherwise, your date could feel uncomfortable.

The next day, send flowers to your host with a note thanking him for the evening. Say that you're sorry and that you did not understand he wanted you to come alone.

Important: Never ask to bring a date to anything other than a cocktail party or large buffet. If the invitation reads "and guest," be sure to let your host know your date's name before the gathering takes place.

•**You get caught in a white lie.** You've canceled a dinner engagement with a colleague, claiming urgent business.

In reality, it was the only night that you could dine with someone else. The problem occurs when a friend of the colleague spots you and tells your colleague.

Strategy: Apologize to your colleague the next day, preferably in person. Say, "If I had told you the truth up front—that this was the only night that I could see this person—I know you would have understood. I was just too embarrassed to tell you."

•**A disparaging remark you make gets back to the person about whom it was directed.** You called a colleague "a jerk" without realizing that his spouse was at your elbow.

Solution: Everything that follows is about damage control. If possible, preempt the problem by immediately taking the spouse aside to apologize before she leaves the group. If she has already left, call their home immediately and speak to both spouses. Be sure to state that you're sorry and that you were nasty without cause. Then explain that you've learned your lesson.

If you have told a lie about the person, send a disclaimer to everyone present when you told the lie.

Gift-Giving Dos and Don'ts

Peggy Post, great-granddaughter-in-law of the etiquette pioneer, Emily Post. She is spokesperson for Emily Post Institute in Burlington, VT, and author of *Emily Post's Etiquette.* HarperCollins. *www.emilypost.com.*

Every holiday season, we receive hundreds of letters at the Emily Post Institute asking about gift-giving etiquette. *Here are the questions we get most often...*

•**Is it OK to "regift"?** Sometimes—but proceed cautiously and follow these guidelines...

•The item must be brand new and in its original package.

•The gift should be something the recipient would love.

•It should not be something the original giver took great care to select or make for you.

•Regifting a nice bottle of wine to a wine lover is fine. Regifting a crystal vase that your mother gave you is not. When in doubt, don't do it.

•**Someone with whom I wasn't planning to exchange gifts gave me one. Do I have to reciprocate?** No. Just thank the gift giver warmly and leave it at that. Otherwise, you may start a new gift-giving tradition that is difficult to break. Of course, if that's what you would like to do, reciprocate!

•**My parents gave me a very expensive television—but it is not the one I wanted. Can I ask them if I can exchange it for a different one?** Just be honest, especially since the gift was extravagant and your parents will expect to see you use it.

First, thank them enthusiastically for the very generous gift. Try to point out something specific that requires you to return it. For example, if it's missing a feature that you were hoping for, gently suggest an exchange. Say something like, "Mom, Dad, this is an amazing gift—but this model doesn't have the surround-sound feature that I think we would really enjoy. Would you mind terribly if I exchanged it?"

•**I've been invited to a holiday party. Should I bring a gift for the host?** Yes, but don't bring anything that distracts the host—food or flowers that need to be taken care of immediately are not the best choices.

Keep the gift simple and the cost below $20—a bottle of wine...a small potted plant...a flower arrangement already in a vase…or perhaps a holiday ornament.

There is one exception. An open house is an informal way to celebrate and doesn't require a gift for the host, though you can certainly bring one if you choose.

•I mail my grandchildren their holiday presents, but they never send thank-you notes. This really bothers me. Should I talk to my son? Start by calling and asking your son or daughter-in-law—or better yet, ask your grandchildren directly—whether the gifts arrived safely. If the answer is yes, drop a hint with, "Well, I'm glad to hear that. Since I didn't hear from you, I was starting to wonder if the packages made it there. Did you like the gifts?"

If you don't think you got your message across, you'll have to be more direct. Talk frankly to your son—or if the grandkids are age eight or older, speak to them. Tell them politely that it's important to you that they express appreciation.

If this doesn't work, you may choose to stop sending gifts. That should get their attention—and teach your grandchildren that thank-you notes mean a lot.

•Should I give my boss a holiday gift? What about the people who report to me and other coworkers? Generally, you shouldn't give a gift to the boss. It could be seen as an attempt to win favor. However, an inexpensive gift that isn't too personal from you and other employees is fine. If you and your boss have worked closely together for years, it's OK to give a small gift.

When you're the boss, it's up to you whether or not to give gifts to your staff. It's certainly a nice gesture and a great way to acknowledge those who work for you.

If you do decide to give gifts, give across the board—don't give to only one department head but not the other two.

Good gift ideas include a nice bottle of wine, gift certificates, CDs and food items.

As for coworkers, a Secret Santa (in which each employee draws a name and gives a gift to that person) or a holiday grab bag are two of the easier ways to handle gift giving.

Food gifts also are a good idea—bring in a batch of homemade cookies or a box of chocolates to share with colleagues.

Nancy Samalin Tells How to Help Your Kids Build the Right Kind of Friendships with the Right Kind of Kids

Nancy Samalin, founder and director of Parent Guidance Workshops, 180 Riverside Dr., New York City 10024. She is author of several books on parenting, including *Loving Your Child Is Not Enough: Positive Discipline that Works.* Penguin.

Parents have much more influence than they think over their children's choice of friends.

But in our attempt to protect our children, it is important to recognize that peer relationships are vital to our children's development. It's the arena in which they learn to make decisions, to lead or follow, to become considerate and loyal and to recover from mistakes.

How to have a positive influence over your children's choice of friends…

•Deemphasize popularity. Many parents unwittingly push kids to make friends. They fret if their children aren't invited to every birthday party. They are devastated whenever their kids are rejected by the "in" crowd.

But when you push for more popularity, your children get the message there is something wrong with them.

Encourage quality over quantity. The number of friends your children have is less important than if they have one or two good friends. And if you emphasize popularity or being part of the clique, your children may become followers who go along blindly with the crowd.

If children are left out—or picked on by their peer group—help them recognize that it is not necessarily their fault. Instead, reassure them that it is normal, though painful, to be "in" one week and "out" the next.

I've found that these popularity contests are more upsetting to parents than to kids. Most kids are more resilient than we give them credit for. Try to ride the waves of friendship fads, remembering that kids are fickle and peer groups are constantly in a state of flux.

•**Don't interfere without good reason.** Unless your children's friends are leading them into potentially hazardous situations, resist meddling in their relationships.

If you suspect that risky behavior is involved, remind your children about your clear, firm rules.

Example: When my kids wanted to go along with peer pressure, a phrase we used was, "Safety is a nonnegotiable issue in this family."

Otherwise, allow children opportunities to negotiate their own issues and differences. Kids need time among themselves to learn how to develop their own rules, to share and take turns, to play fair and square, to recover from bruised egos.

Certainly there are times and places for adult supervision, but try to intervene selectively.

•**Listen to your child.** The stronger your children's self-confidence, the better they'll be able to resist negative influences of peers.

Help strengthen children's egos by listening attentively when they're having trouble with friends.

Don't jump right in with ready-made solutions or criticism. Invite children to tell you what happened before you overreact…and then listen. They're not likely to open up if you go through the roof.

Example: Your son comes home in tears because his friends ridiculed him for backing out of a scheme to shoplift.

Don't immediately yell, "You're not spending time with those kids ever again." Instead, listen to his anguish about being ridiculed. Encourage him to talk about his feelings, and praise him for being strong and taking an unpopular stand.

You might say, "I know that was tough. It took a lot of courage not to go along with the guys. I'm wondering, though, if these are kids you *really* enjoy being with."

Try to determine whether your child is afraid of being left out. If that's the problem, help build up his/her self-confidence by praising him when he shows independent thinking.

•**Encourage individuality.** Keep in mind that you and your child have different tastes and opinions.

He may be attracted to people to whom you don't relate at all, just as you and he probably don't share the same tastes in food, music or movies.

Try to respect your children's differences even when you don't like the friends they keep.

Helpful: Encourage children to make choices and solve problems…ask their opinions about people you meet, TV shows and articles and books you read together.

When your child mentions a new best friend, don't grill him with lots of intrusive questions. Withhold your judgment.

Even if you don't like his choice of friends, don't automatically denigrate him, especially without any evidence of harmful behavior.

•**Encourage children to stick up for themselves.** Help your children practice this skill by allowing them to disagree with you in reasonable ways.

That doesn't mean tolerating sassy back talk or outright defiance, but it does mean supporting their self-expression.

Example: When your daughter insists that she must have a pair of expensive sneakers because all her friends are wearing them…or when she begs you to let her stay out with peers past her curfew… give her a chance to express her reasons for asking.

You don't have to agree, but show respect for her opinions. You might say, "Well, I'm ready to listen—try to convince me…" or "Let me hear your point of view…"

Even if you disagree with her, you are giving her opportunities to think for herself and evaluate her options.

If you decide that your child should not stay out past her curfew or that you cannot afford to buy her those expensive sneakers, reassure her that she can still be part of the group.

Point out that the other kids will still invite her to play basketball in her old sneakers or that she'll be able to go off with her friends on other excursions—even though she must be home by 9 pm on this particular night.

By supporting children in voicing and defending their opinions, you help them practice a skill that they can also use with their peers.

They will become more confident about saying no the next time friends try to lead them toward misbehavior or toward values that are unacceptable to you.

How to Get Back On Schedule When You're Always Running Behind

Stephanie Winston, time-management consultant and editor of *Stephanie Winston's The Organized Executive*, Georgetown Publishing House, 1101 30 St. NW, Washington, DC 20007.

Even the most efficient people frequently feel as if they are constantly running behind schedule.

Here's how to overcome the diversions that prevent you from accomplishing as much as you would like to each day...

• **Catch your breath and start to plan.** One of the biggest enemies of good time management is poor planning.

The more rushed you feel, the less productive you'll be. The more frantic you are, the less decisive you will be.

Helpful: Go into the office one hour earlier than usual one day a week...or stay one hour later. Spend the time writing down your three most important priorities. Then set deadlines for each of them and create a manageable to-do list that prioritizes the tasks.

• **Use peak time wisely.** Tackle your toughest or least pleasant projects when you feel most productive.

The best time of day for most people is early in the morning, when they are least distracted and most motivated.

Your hardest tasks should be slotted for the early hours. Once this work is out of the way, you can make better use of the remaining hours of the day.

• **Know when to run and hide.** Sometimes you need absolute silence to concentrate on what needs to get done. Sitting in your office—with the door open or closed—isn't always the best solution.

Better: Commandeer an empty conference room or head out to a coffee shop. Distraction-free time—even if it's just 15 minutes to a half-hour—is powerful when used to refocus on what needs to be done.

• **Just say *no*—very politely.** Interruptions by people who need your help can throw you off track. While you can't stop these requests, they can be controlled.

Helpful: Learn to deflect assignments when you're too busy. Try saying, "I'm just snowed under right now." If you really can't say no, take on only part of the assignment—and not all of it.

• **Delegate down—and down.** Some of my clients would be less overwhelmed if they identified and delegated the less important areas of their jobs.

The key is to start thinking of the people who work with you—and this can include your boss—as your helpers. They are there to help you get things done so that you can be more efficient and productive.

Don't be so obsessed with setting things right that you can't let go of an assignment.

Never feel guilty about backing off and using resources to reach your goals at work.

• **Keep track of interruptions.** Some people are overwhelmed when they are at work because subordinates ask them for more guidance than they should.

Others spend too much time talking to friends or family members. Some may pay too much attention to the stock market.

Helpful: Keep a running list of interruptions, the topic and how long you were distracted. Review this list every day to see where you can limit your availability and willingness to give up precious time.

• **Cut down on business travel.** Most business travel is a waste of time.

While it is important to travel to make a presentation or close a deal, many of your trips away from the office and home aren't as critical as you think.

Before you agree to attend a conference or to go out of town to meet with people, ask yourself what you could accomplish if you remained at the office.

Unnecessary business travel and "networking" actually make you less efficient and distract you from what's truly important—your staff's needs and your company's goals.

Protect Yourself from Kitchen Sponges

Kitchen sponges harbor large numbers of germs. To avoid contact with these potentially infectious microbes, use paper towels…or rinse the sponge, wring it out and microwave it for 30 to 60 seconds.

Dean O. Cliver, PhD, professor of food safety, School of Veterinary Medicine, University of California, Davis.

Cleanliness is Next to…

Toilet seats are up to a million times cleaner than dish cloths. Chopping boards, sinks and kitchen countertops are also dirtier than toilet seats—which are too dry to support a thriving population of bacteria. To clean a dish cloth, soak it for 10 minutes in diluted bleach (one cup in a sinkful of water).

Pat Rusin, PhD, research scientist, department of soil, water and environmental science, University of Arizona, Tucson.

Spill Something In the Oven?

Immediately sprinkle an oven spill with a mixture of one part cinnamon to six parts salt. This mixture will absorb the spill and eliminate the burnt odor. Once the oven has cooled, wipe up the mixture.

Graham and Rosemary Haley, household task experts, Toronto, and authors of *Haley's Cleaning Hints: A Compilation.* New American.

When to Buy Gas

Buy gas early in the week. In times of rising prices, service stations typically raise the cost per gallon on Friday so they can profit from weekend traffic.

Buying at the beginning of the week should get you the lowest price of that week.

Geoff Sundstrom, spokesman, AAA, Heathrow, FL.